Real World Math
Engaging Students through Global Issues

Student Workbook

Facing
THE Future™

Real World Math
Engaging Students through Global Issues
Student Workbook

Copyright © 2009 *Facing the Future*

ISBN 978-0-9815577-3-1

This book was printed on recycled content paper using soy-based inks.

Facing the Future is a nonprofit organization dedicated to educating and motivating today's students to be responsible stewards of tomorrow's world. We develop and deliver standards-based hands-on lessons, student textbooks, curriculum units, and professional development opportunities for educators that promote critical thinking on global issues, sustainability and positive solutions. *Facing the Future* curriculum is in use in all 50 U.S. states and over 85 countries by teachers and students in grades K-12, in undergraduate and graduate classes, and across multiple subject areas.

For more information, visit www.facingthefuture.org.

FACING THE FUTURE
811 First Avenue, Suite 454
Seattle, WA 98104
(206) 264-1503
www.facingthefuture.org

We dedicate this book
to Anne Fox,
whose tireless dedication
to education for
sustainability
inspires us.

Contributions and Thanks

This book was developed in alignment with national and state mathematics education standards, and with the input of a number of mathematics experts and educators. The standards addressed are indicated for each lesson, and all references are listed at the end of the text.

The following individuals provided expert advice and feedback on this text:

Suzanne Alejandre
Director of Professional Development, The Math Forum @ Drexel

Boo Drury

Dr. David Moursund
Professor Emeritus, College of Education, University of Oregon

Laura Tyler
Curriculum Coordinator, Washington MESA

Primary Curriculum Developers
Sheeba Jacob, MEd
Laura Skelton, MS

Layout and Graphic Design
DECODE, Inc.

Copy Editing
BLUEPRINT EDITORIAL

The following educators reviewed, edited, and otherwise contributed to this text:

Char Alkire
Former Science Educator and Teacher Supervisor

Matthew John Brewer
Teacher, Eckstein Middle School

Wendy Church, PhD
Facing the Future

Ava Erickson
Faculty, Seattle Girls' School

Beth Hintz, MS
Facing the Future

Jessica C Levine
Teacher, Eckstein Middle School

Cecilia Lund, MS
Facing the Future

Anne Metcalfe
Retired Educator

Kristin Moore
Department Chair, Explorer West Middle School

Sandi Phinney, MPA

Kim Rakow Bernier, MPA
Facing the Future

David White-Espin
Teacher, Secondary Bilingual Orientation Center

Cate White, MPA

Dave Wilton, MEd
Facing the Future

Facing the Future Advisory Council

Char Alkire
Former Science Educator and Teacher Supervisor

Jamie Bender
Outreach Coordinator,
Center for International Studies,
University of Chicago

Jim Bennett
Vice President,
Cinematch, Netflix Inc.

John de Graaf
PBS Producer and Author, *Affluenza*

Dee Dickinson
Founder and CEO,
New Horizons for Learning

Wendy Ewbank
Teacher,
Seattle Girls' School

Scott Jamieson
Teacher,
Lakeside School

Marie Marrs
Retired Global Sustainability and Language Arts Teacher

Kate McPherson
Director,
Project Service Leadership

Abby Ruskey
Executive Director,
Environmental Education Association of Washington

Dr. Debra Sullivan
President,
Praxis Institute for Early Childhood Education

Dr. Anand Yang
Director,
Jackson School of International Studies,
University of Washington

Field Testing

Thank you to the following teachers and their students for field testing these materials:

Dr. Carol T. Benson
Mathematics Teacher,
University High School,
Illinois State University

Erica Bergamini
Mathematics and Science Teacher,
The Northwest School

Tim Bombaci
Mathematics and Science Teacher,
Manson Elementary School

Tracy Corell
Mathematics and Science Teacher,
LaSalle Middle School

Claire Crocker
Mathematics Teacher,
Lincoln Middle School

Kevin Dykema
Mathematics Teacher,
Mattawan Middle School

Angie Flynn
Mathematics and Science Teacher,
Community Preparatory School

Tina Gay
Gifted Teacher,
K. E. Taylor Elementary School

Cynthia Kline
Special Education Teacher,
RM Teitelman School

Constance McAninch
Middle School Math Teacher,
Cairo American College

Heidi Rudolph
Mathematics Instructor,
Orange High School

Rich Santoro
Mathematics Teacher,
T. Roosevelt High School

George Simmons
Science Teacher,
RM Teitelman School

Craig Snell
IB Mathematics Teacher,
International School of Phnom Penh

Sue Solomon
Mathematics Teacher,
Riverside Middle School

Amy U. Spies
Mathematics Teacher,
Community Learning Center East

Donna Szemcsak
Mathematics Teacher,
RM Teitelman School

Joanne Tester
Student Teacher,
RM Teitelman School

Laura Vinyard
Mathematics Teacher,
Jordan Middle School

Introduction

When introduced to new mathematics concepts, you may have thought, "When will I ever use this?" or "How does this relate to my life?" *Real World Math: Engaging Students through Global Issues* will pique your interest by providing real data on global issues with a focus on practical solutions.

Foundational algebra and geometry skills are taught here within the context of global issues and sustainability. Sustainability refers to the ability of current generations to meet their needs without limiting the ability of future generations to meet their needs. You will investigate issues like quality of life, community resource distribution, educational attainment, and waste/recycling trends.

These investigations will encourage you to build on your mathematics knowledge while simultaneously using 21st-century skills, such as critical thinking, collaborating with your peers, and looking at problems from a global perspective. These combined skills will help prepare you for the future, where you will encounter problem-solving situations similar to these.

Your teacher will have a guidebook to assist you in getting started. The teacher's guide includes 15 lessons that were inspired, researched, designed, and field tested by mathematics teachers and other education professionals. Lessons are aligned with learning standards developed by the National Council of Teachers of Mathematics. Your teacher also has access to other real world data sets, extension problems, and action projects to further support practical explorations in math.

This workbook includes handouts, supplemental worksheets, and topical sustainability readings that correspond with the lessons in the teacher's guide. These resources will help you to learn more about these topics and what you can do to shape tomorrow's world.

This workbook is a tool to help you build the knowledge and skills needed to solve problems big and small. Enjoy these investigations!

Table of Contents

Table of Contents, *continued*

Name _____   Date _____

Waste Not, Want Not, page 1

Objectives

- Identify number patterns
- Construct expressions that contain variables to represent real-world patterns
- Use tables and graphs to organize data
- Explore patterns of waste disposal and recycling in the United States

Investigations

1. Did you know that 2 million plastic bottles are used every 5 minutes in the United States?[1] Review the following data and complete the table, using the pattern shown.

Number of Bottles Used Every 5 Minutes in the United States

Time (in minutes)	5	10	15	20	25	30	35	40	45	50	55	60
Bottles (in millions)	2	4	6	8	10	12	14	16	18	20	22	24

2. How many plastic bottles are used in 1 day?

3. If $\frac{1}{3}$ of plastic bottles are recycled daily in the United States, how many bottles each day are NOT recycled?

4. What might be 2 potential consequences, either positive or negative, of NOT recycling plastic bottles?

5. Create an equation to represent the number of bottles recycled for any number of hours, using h to represent the number of hours and b to represent the number of bottles.

6. Now look at the amount of waste generated per person in a single day in the United States.[2] Organize the data in the table below on a line graph.

Year	1960	1970	1980	1990	2000
Pounds per Person per Day	2.7	3.3	3.7	4.5	4.6

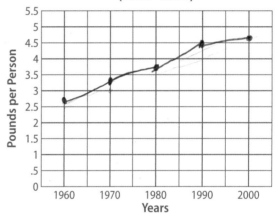

Pounds per Person per Day (1960–2000)

7. Using your graph, predict the number of pounds per day the average person will discard in 2020.

Waste Not, Want Not, page 2

8. Look at the following circle graph of the materials we discard.[3] A circle graph shows how different parts of a whole are divided.

Materials in Waste Stream

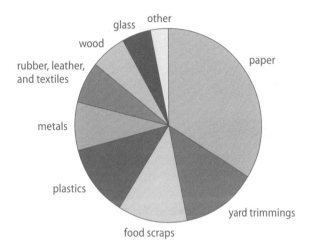

If all materials other than plastics and food scraps = 76% of our waste stream and the percentage of plastics is equal to the percentage of food scraps, what percentage of our waste stream is plastics?

9. Recycling 4,050 20-ounce plastic bottles saves 1 cubic yard of landfill space.[4] How many plastic bottles would need to be recycled to save 50 cubic yards of landfill space?

10. Recycling materials is one way to combat climate change. In 2006, 7 million metric tons of metals were recycled, eliminating greenhouse gas emissions equivalent to 6.5 million metric tons of carbon dioxide.[5] (Carbon dioxide is a greenhouse gas that leads to warmer temperatures on Earth.)

If we tripled the amount of metals we recycle, how many million metric tons of carbon dioxide will be eliminated?

Bonus

In 2006, 32.5% of all solid waste was recycled, amounting to 81.8 million tons of recycled materials.[6] What was the total amount of solid waste generated in 2006 (including recycled and discarded materials)? Report your answer in millions of tons.

Practice with Patterns

1. Review and complete the following tables.

Table I: 2 million plastic bottles are used every 5 minutes in the United States. Complete the following table to see the pattern of bottle use over time:

Time (in minutes)	5	10	15	20	25	30
Bottles (in millions)	2	4	6			

Table II: Now consider a different pattern, and complete the following table:

Time (in minutes)	5	10	15	20	25	30
Bottles (in millions)	2	4	8			

2. What is happening in Table II?

3. Why might bottle usage in the future follow the pattern in Table II rather than the pattern in Table I?

> **Exponential growth** is demonstrated by the pattern in Table II, where usage is increasing faster and faster over time.

4. Data from Tables I and II are shown on the graph below. Complete the graph using the numbers you added to Table II. The resulting double bar graph will allow you to compare steady growth (Table I) to exponential growth (Table II).

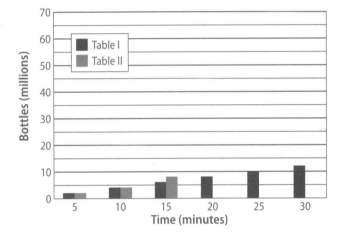

Bottles Used over Time

What's the Big Deal?

Want to know how you can save natural resources, energy, and money all at the same time? The answer might be simpler than you think—you can save all three by reusing and recycling.

Did you know that it takes 3 tons of wood and over 19,000 gallons of water to make 1 ton of paper?[1] What about the fact that recycling aluminum cans uses 95% less energy than mining new aluminum?[2] And recycling plastics means using less petroleum oil and releasing fewer toxic chemicals into the air.

According to the Environmental Protection Agency, the average American generates 4.6 pounds of trash each day. That amounts to about 700,000 tons of trash generated in the United States daily. When you consider that household trash accounts for only 2% of the waste generated in the United States, you start seeing just how large the issue of waste disposal really is![3]

Where It All Goes

When we put trash in a trash can or dumpster to be carried away, the trash does not simply disappear. It typically travels to a landfill or an incinerator. A landfill is a facility where waste is essentially buried in the ground. Landfills are lined with strong plastic, along with natural materials such as clay, to keep our trash from harming the soil and groundwater. Unfortunately, all plastic liners eventually leak and release waste materials into the environment.[4] This can harm people and other species by contaminating groundwater we use for drinking and soils that grow our food.

Incinerators are another type of waste disposal facility. Incinerators burn solid waste and produce ash that is sent to a landfill. Some incinerators are used to produce energy for electricity. Both incinerators and landfills have negative environmental consequences such as air and groundwater pollution.

> "We buy a wastebasket and take it home in a plastic bag. Then we take the wastebasket out of the bag, and put the bag in the wastebasket."
>
> —Lily Tomlin, comedian

Don't Waste a Good Thing

There are many ways that you can reduce waste and protect Earth's resources. Here are some tips:

- Swap clothes, books, and videos with friends rather than buy new ones.
- Recycle and buy products made from recycled materials.
- Choose products with minimal packaging materials.

Reducing waste and recycling have more than just environmental benefits. You can save money by reusing items or buying lightly used items. Also, recycling and purchasing recycled products provide jobs for the people who turn our "trash" into something we can actually use.[5]

---

1 Estimates made using the Environmental Defense Fund Paper Calculator, www.papercalculator.org.
2 Natural Resources Defense Council, "Too Good to Throw Away," February 1997, www.nrdc.org/cities/recycling/recyc/recyinx.asp.
3 Elizabeth Royte, *Garbage Land: On the Secret Trail of Trash* (New York: Little, Brown and Company, 2005), 275.
4 Ibid., 57.
5 U.S. Environmental Protection Agency, "Puzzled About Recycling's Value? Look Beyond the Bin," January 1998, www.epa.gov/osw/conserve/downloads/benefits.pdf.

Microcredit Business Plan,[1] page 1

Objectives

- Evaluate formulas for different values
- Solve multistep equations
- Investigate microcredit as a potential solution to extreme poverty

Background Information	
Country	India
Currency	rupee
Exchange Rate	43 rupees = US $1
Product/Business	cycle repair shop

Costs	
Start-up costs (Sc) *Start-up costs include what you need to start or expand your business, such as equipment and tools. These are one-time expenses.*	800 rupees
Monthly costs (Mc) *Monthly costs include what you need to spend each month to keep your business going.*	1,300 rupees

Profits	
Amount of money you expect to make in sales each month	3,500 rupees

1. Calculate your total operational costs (TOC) using the following equation, where n = number of months: $TOC = Sc + n \times Mc$

Number of Months	Total Operational Costs
1	
6	
12	

2. Calculate your profit (P) for a given period of time using the following equation, where S = monthly sales, Mc = monthly costs, and n = number of months: $P = n(S - Mc)$

Number of Months	Profit
1	
6	
12	
18	

3. What do you notice about the profit in the given amount of time that you calculated? Explain your thinking in 2-3 sentences.

4. Convert the number of rupees made in 1 year to U.S. dollars.

Microcredit Business Plan, page 2

5. What is your expected *net* profit after 6 months?

(Hint: To find the net product, subtract your start-up costs)

6. Interest is the money that a lender charges to borrowers; it is usually a percentage of the loan amount. When repaying a loan, borrowers must pay interest in addition to the principal loan amount.

For a principal loan amount of 2,000 rupees loaned at an annual interest rate of 20%, calculate how much interest (I) you will need to pay back for different periods of time. Use the following equation, where p = principal loan amount, r = interest rate, and t = time in years: $I = p \times r \times t$

(Hint: You will need to convert the interest rate, 20%, into the decimal 0.20 to solve the equation)

Number of Years	Interest
1	
2	
3	

Bonus

A lending organization has raised $4,000 that it wants to use to provide $100 microloans to people in one community. Of the $4,000 raised, $500 must be used for program administration costs (to pay for paperwork and salaries for people who will help set up the loans). How many microcredit loans can be provided with the organization's $4,000?

Practice with Algebra

Algebra is a branch of mathematics that uses letters to represent variables, or unknown values. The following algebraic equation includes the variable, x.

Example: $3x = 42$

Solving an **algebraic equation** allows us to find the value of the variable. How would you solve the previous equation?

You might solve it with mental math. Or you might use inverse operations. For example, to isolate x from 3, you could divide **both** sides by 3.

$$\frac{3x}{3} = \frac{42}{3}$$

$$x = 14$$

Sandra lives in Guatemala. She is applying for a microcredit loan to start a street food business. **Microcredit** is a system of lending people very small amounts of money. Complete the following calculations to determine Sandra's anticipated costs and profits.

1. Start-up costs for the business include buying a cart for selling the food on the street, a freezer, and bulk foods. The cart costs $65, and the freezer costs $900. The total start-up cost is $1053. Write an equation to represent the start-up costs, assigning a variable for the bulk foods.

2. Solve your equation to find the cost of the bulk foods Sandra plans to buy.

3. Sandra calculates her monthly costs (C) to be $415, and she expects monthly sales (S) to be $700. Calculate her profit (P) for a 6-month period using the following equation, where n represents the number of months:
$P = n(S - C)$

4. Sandra wants to use a portion of her profits to invest in community health care projects, including funding health education and a community clinic. She decides to give $125 each month to health care projects. Which of the following equations best represents this situation?
   a) $P = n(S - 125 - C)$
   b) $P = n(S - C + 125)$
   c) $P + 125 = n(S - C)$

5. Explain why the other 2 equations are incorrect.

6. A microcredit loan business is so impressed by Sandra's business plan that they decide to give her an additional $100 per month to include in her monthly sales. What is the amount of sales she will now be able to earn in 1 year?

Poverty by the Numbers

Can you imagine spending several hours each day walking for miles to obtain the water that you need? What if you only had $2 a day to purchase necessities like food? Could you live comfortably? What would you have to give up?

Nobody chooses to be poor. Yet many people in our world live in poverty. Over 2.5 billion people live on less than $2 per day.[1] Imagine what it is like to be Jyoti, a 13-year-old girl in India who lives in a mud house. Jyoti lives in poverty. Her village has no electricity, running water, or doctor. She works all day instead of attending school. What do you think Jyoti's future looks like? What can Jyoti do to improve her living conditions?

Fighting Poverty through Microcredit

In 1976, an economics professor named Muhammad Yunus was visiting very poor households in Bangladesh, a country in South Asia, when he realized that very small loans (just $100) could lift people out of poverty. In 1983 Yunus helped found the Grameen Bank to provide loans to poor Bangladeshis. Since the Grameen Bank was founded, it has loaned money to more than 7 million people.[2]

This system of providing very small loans to people in poverty is called *microcredit*. Microcredit is one tool that can help to break the cycle of poverty. As with any other form of credit, borrowers pay back the loaned money, with interest. A microcredit borrower might buy the materials to open a small store selling basic household supplies, or buy a pot and ingredients for selling simple snack foods on the street. Some borrowers take out additional loans to expand their businesses.

The resulting income improves borrowers' lives, allowing people to pay for sufficient food, education, homes, and medicine. Successful microcredit programs improve the economic well-being of whole communities. Women, who receive the majority of these loans, often use their earnings to support their families and surrounding communities. In a 1998 study, the World Bank found that extreme poverty fell 70% within five years among borrowers of the Grameen Bank's microcredit program in Bangladesh.[3] Microcredit programs have branched out to many parts of the world, including the United States.

Imagine how Jyoti's life might change if her mother received a loan to buy a cow in order to sell milk and cheese.

> **"Give a man a fish, he'll eat for a day. Give a woman microcredit, she, her husband, her children and her extended family will eat for a lifetime."**
> —**Bono**, humanitarian and musician

What You Can Do

There are many ways to combat the cycle of poverty:
- Organize a fundraiser and send the proceeds to an organization that aids those in poverty. Just a few such organizations are BeadforLife, Water Partners International, and Trickle Up.
- Volunteer at an organization dedicated to fighting poverty.
- Work with youth around the world to come up with creative solutions for helping people to lift themselves out of poverty.

1 The World Bank, "Poverty Data," *Supplement to World Development Indicators 2008*, 2008, http://web.worldbank.org/WBSITE/ EXTERNAL/DATASTATISTICS/0,,contentMDK:21725423~pagePK:64 133150~piPK:64133175~theSitePK:239419,00.html

2 Grameen Bank, "Grameen Bank at a Glance," www.grameen-info.org/index.php?option=com_content&task=view&id=26&Itemid=175 (accessed December 1, 2008).

3 RESULTS, "2007 Basics: Global Economic Empowerment Campaign," www.results.org/website/article.asp?id=2567 (accessed December 10, 2008).

The Ups and Downs of Population, page 1

Objectives

- Add integers with same and different signs
- Solve equations with integers
- Plot integers on a coordinate plane
- Examine population trends for Japan and India
- Consider some consequences of positive and negative population growth

Investigations

1. Answer the following questions to see what you already know about population growth.

   a. Do you think most countries have growing or declining populations?

   b. Name 1 thing that might lead to a population increase.

   c. Name 1 thing that might cause population to decline.

2. Look at the age-gender structure of Japan in 2000:[1]

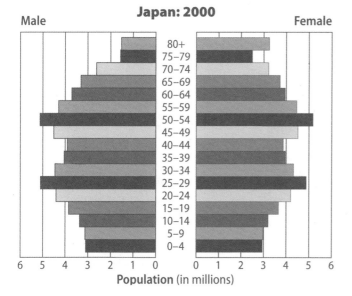

Japan: 2000

Male | Female

Population (in millions)

   a. In 2000, were most people in Japan young, old, or somewhere in between?

   b. How do you think the age structure of Japan will be different in 50 years?

3. Use the information provided in the following table to calculate the number of people in each age group in 2050. Use the following equation to find Population Totals for 2050, where P_{2050} is Population Totals for 2050, P_{2000} is Population Totals for 2000, and C is Change in Population from 2000 to 2050:

$$P_{2050} = P_{2000} + C$$

Change in Population by Age Group in Japan from 2000 to 2050

Age	Population Totals for 2000	Change in Population from 2000 to 2050	Population Totals for 2050
0–9	12,142,579	−5,515,470	
10–19	14,057,715	−6,645,674	
20–29	18,580,447	−10,641,656	
30–39	16,776,034	−8,170,921	
40–49	16,789,176	−6,124,838	
50–59	19,041,467	−7,376,268	
60–69	14,679,053	−1,940,665	
70–79	9,890,833	+4,687,353	
80+	4,771,919	+8,672,742	

4. Add the *Change in Population from 2000 to 2050* numbers for ages 50–80+. Based on your answer, how will the number of people older than 50 change from 2000 to 2050?

5. Which 10-year age group will lose the greatest number of people from 2000 to 2050?

6. What is 1 way that the predicted population structure for 2050 might affect Japan?

The Ups and Downs of Population, page 2

7. Look at the age-gender structure predicted for India for 2050. Describe in 1-2 sentences how the population in India will differ from Japan's population in 2050.

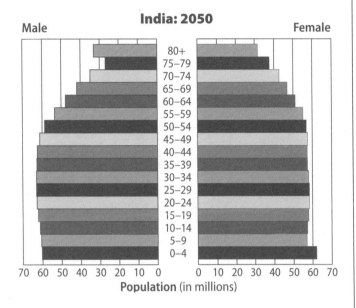

India: 2050

Male   Female

Population (in millions)

8. What is 1 way that the predicted population structure for 2050 might affect India?

9. Japan's population growth rate is -0.139%.[2] What integer is closest to the numeric value of -0.139%?

10. Plot the coordinate pairs in the following table on a coordinate plane in order to see a visual representation of how Japan's population is changing. The x-values are 5-year time intervals. The y-values represent changes in population in millions of people, rounded to the nearest million.

Time (x) 1990–2050	Change in Population (y)
1990	0
1995	2
2000	3
2005	4
2010	3
2015	1
2020	−3
2025	−7
2030	−11
2035	−16
2040	−21
2045	−26
2050	−31

11. What is the trend of the graph you created? Explain your observations in 1-2 sentences.

Bonus

Given that India's population growth rate is $+1.578\%$,[3] create an algebraic equation to determine future population size in India, where x represents the current population and y represents the future population. Then solve your equation for $x = 1$ billion.

Practice with Integers

Positive and negative whole numbers and 0 are all **integers**.

Absolute value of any number is the distance between that number and 0 on the number line. For example, both -4 and 4 are the same distance from 0 on the number line.

So the absolute value of both -4 and 4 is 4. Absolute value is indicated by 2 vertical bars on either side of a number: $|-4|$ and $|4|$

1. Consider a place called Sunspot Island. Each year the population doubles, or multiplies by 2. Complete the following table to show the growth of the island's population over a 10-year period.

Year	Population
1	200
2	
3	
4	
5	
6	
7	
8	
9	
10	

2. Suppose there is only enough land on the island to grow food for 200,000 people. What will happen to Sunspot Island and its people in a very short time? Think of at least 2 possible impacts of population growth on the environmental resources and people of Sunspot.

3. In year 12, a disease begins to reduce the population of Sunspot Island. Then, in year 14, a civil war breaks out, resulting in many deaths. Perform the calculations in the middle column to discover how the population changes each year.

Year	Perform These Calculations	Resulting Population
11	$-100,000(-2) =$	
12	$170,000 + (-20,000) =$	
13	$-240,000 \div (-2) =$	
14	$83,500 - 8,600 =$	
15	$|-2| \times 37,450 =$	

4. Explain what appears to be happening to Sunspot's population in year 15.

Increasing Numbers

Handwritten annotations: "What caused the human pop. Increase?", "Needs extra Room", "more than 2× more", "Jeans hill pop.l"

"The hungry world cannot be fed until and unless the growth of its resources and the growth of its population come into balance."
—Lyndon B. Johnson, 36th U.S. President

How many students attend your school? Imagine that the population of students in your school doubles but you still have to stay in the same building. Would your school be able to handle "business as usual" with twice the number of students? What kinds of things would need to change to make room for all the extra people?

About sixty years ago, there were 2.5 billion people living on Earth. It took nearly all of human history—from prehistoric time until after World War II—for the world's population to reach that number. Now that number has more than doubled to over 6.6 billion people, with about 80 million people added to the planet each year. That's like adding another Germany every year or another San Francisco every three and a half days.

Experts who study population growth predict that by 2050 there will be over 9 billion people living in the area where more than 6.6 billion of us live now.[1] With almost half of the world's population under age twenty-five (including you), world population will increase by several billion when those young people start having families.[2]

Currently 95% of all population growth occurs in developing countries such as India and China. Meanwhile, shrinking populations are predicted for some developed countries, such as Japan, Russia, and the nations of Europe.[3]

Causes and Impacts of a Growing Population

Of the 5.2 billion people living in developing countries, statistics show that approximately 60% do not have access to basic sanitation, 25% do not have adequate housing, 20% do not have access to necessary health services, and 20% of children do not have a fifth grade education.[4]

Given these harsh realities, people in these countries may rely on large extended families to make a living and to care for the elderly. Because disease and malnutrition (inadequate or unbalanced nutrition) kill many children before they grow up, large families are often seen as a necessity. This tends to keep population growth rates up.

Solutions

By making specific choices, we can create a future that is both healthy and sustainable for all of us. For example, reducing consumption of natural resources such as timber, freshwater, and fossil fuels throughout the world could increase the amount of resources available to the entire population. Thus, more people would have access to limited resources. When you draw connections between different global issues and create personal solutions to these issues, you are making it possible for future generations to meet their needs.

1 U.S. Census Bureau (www.census.gov), CIA World Factbook (https://www.cia.gov/library/publications/the-world-factbook/), and Population Reference Bureau (www.prb.org).
2 United Nations Population Fund (UNFPA), "State of World Population 2003," www.unfpa.org/swp/2003/swpmain.htm.
3 United Nations Department of Economic and Social Affairs (ESA), "World Population Prospects: The 2004 Revision," www.un.org/esa/population/publications/WPP2004/wpp2004.htm.
4 United Nations Population Fund, "The State of World Population 2001," www.unfpa.org/swp/2001/english/ch01.html.

You Are What You Eat, page 1

Objectives

- Write and solve multi-step equations
- Use tables to solve real-life problems
- Recognize the connection between health, nutrition, and exercise
- Understand that daily choices can affect an individual's well-being

Investigations

Read the following case study with a partner:

Estelle M. is an eighth grade student. She plays on the basketball team and takes great pride in being the point guard. Recently, she hasn't been playing to her best ability. She has felt extremely tired and can't seem to concentrate in class. Even during practice, she is lethargic. This makes her nervous because the team has the potential to win the championships. To win the championships, everyone, including Estelle, needs to be playing her best.

Estelle's mom decides to take her to the doctor. The doctor tells her that her participation in strenuous exercise is great, but he worries that she isn't eating enough calories to support her high activity level. Her doctor asks her to keep track of her caloric intake and the amount of basketball she plays daily.

1. Estelle weighs 150 pounds, and she needs a minimum of 2,560 calories per day to maintain her weight. Her doctor explained that when she plays full court basketball, she burns extra calories. Therefore, she should consume more than 2,560 calories on days when she plays full court basketball. Her doctor suggested that she consume about 11 extra calories for each minute of strenuous exercise.

   Create an equation that Estelle can use to determine how many total calories she needs to eat in a day for a certain amount of exercise.

2. Yesterday, Estelle played basketball for 2 hours. She ate 3,100 calories worth of food. Did Estelle consume enough calories?

3. If Estelle plays basketball for 1 hour per day for the next 5 days, how many calories will she need to consume over that 5-day period? Write and solve an equation showing the number of calories Estelle needs to consume in these 5 days.

You Are What You Eat, page 2

Estelle's doctor explains to her that he thinks she may not be consuming an adequate amount of calories and nutrients. Empty calorie foods have many calories but very few nutrients. High nutrient foods have a much greater amount of recommended daily nutrients (more than 20%), such as iron, calcium, and vitamin C.

While Estelle is exhausted by the end of practice, she has noticed that her teammate Staci still has a lot of energy. She decides to compare her lunch with Staci's to see if Staci's high energy might be related to the calories or nutrients she takes in.[1]

Estelle's Lunch

Item	Calories	% Daily Value
Hamburger	279 calories	Calcium: 6% Vitamin C: 3% Iron: 15%
French fries	539 calories	Calcium: 2% Vitamin C: 8% Iron: 13%
Soda	210 calories	Calcium: 0% Vitamin C: 0% Iron: 0%
1 cupcake	100 calories	Calcium: 10% Vitamin C: 0% Iron: 0%

Staci's Lunch

Item	Calories	% Daily Value
Turkey and cheese sandwich	361 calories	Calcium: 22% Vitamin C: 12% Iron: 13%
Spinach salad (with tomatoes, croutons, and dressing)	_196_ calories	Calcium: 27% Vitamin C: 94% Iron: 42%
2% milk (2 cups)	244 calories	Calcium: _96_ Vitamin C: 1% Iron: 0%
2 bananas	400 calories	Calcium: 1% Vitamin C: 33% Iron: 3%

4. A serving of French fries contains 539 calories. The amount of calories in a spinach salad (s) can be found by solving the following equation, where f is the number of calories in French fries: $s = \frac{1}{2}(f) + 16.5$.

   Solve the equation to determine the number of calories in a spinach salad.

5. Staci's lunch provides her with 108% of her daily calcium. What is the % daily value of calcium contained in the 2 cups of milk she drinks for lunch?

6. Calculate the difference in Estelle's and Staci's calories and percent daily values of calcium, vitamin C, and iron.

7. Based on your calculations, what are some possible reasons that Staci has more energy than Estelle at the end of practice?

8. Both Staci and Estelle are much less active during the summer, when they are not playing basketball daily. How do you think their caloric intake should be adjusted for summer months?

Practice with Solving Equations

When solving an equation to find the value of a **variable**, you must isolate the variable, or put it by itself on one side of the equal sign. To do this, you can use inverse operations. Remember to perform the same operations on **both** sides of the equation. Here is an example:

$$3b + 24 = 42$$

$$3b + 24 - 24 = 42 - 24 \quad \longleftarrow \text{ **Step 1:** Subtract 24 from both sides.}$$

$$3b = 18$$

$$3b \div 3 = 18 \div 3 \quad \longleftarrow \text{ **Step 2:** Divide both sides by 3.}$$

$$b = 6$$

1. Janice runs track. In 1 day, she burned 600 calories during a strenuous practice, which was a quarter of the total calories she ate that day. Write an algebraic equation for this situation, using a variable to represent total calories.

2. Solve your equation to find the total number of calories Janice consumed.

3. Charlotte and Jesse monitor their daily intake of iron. Iron is an important nutrient that helps give your body energy for physical activity. On Monday, Charlotte consumed 3 times less iron than Jesse did. The total amount of iron they both consumed on Monday was 36 mg. Set up an equation for this situation. Then, find the amount of iron each of them consumed.

4. In many places around the world, rice is one of the main components of people's diets. If 1 cup of rice = 205 calories, determine the amount of calories consumed in 2 separate meals that include rice (r equals the number of calories in 1 cup of rice).

   a. $2r + 11 =$ _____ calories in meal

   b. $4(r - 75) =$ _____ calories in meal

5. If a 175-pound man who exercises daily needs over 3000 calories to maintain a constant weight,[1] would either of the meals in problem #4 be a good choice? Why or why not?

Handwritten annotations (top): Why do they know people eat bad if nonsicovers?

Handwritten annotations (left margin): Every one wants to be healthy · why do you eat healthy · Eat unhealthy · caused disease

What to Eat?

What if you had the chance to design every meal that you ate for the upcoming week? What types of food would you choose? Would your choices be based on nutritional content, cost, or taste?

Being healthy is something that everyone around the world cares about. Without good health, other desirable aspects of a good quality of life—sufficient income, a good education, and time spent with friends and family—are worth little.

What we eat affects our health. When we consume adequate nutrients such as carbohydrates, proteins, and minerals, our bodies become stronger.[1] When people do not get sufficient nutrients, they suffer from a condition called malnutrition. This is especially a problem in the world's poorer nations. Around 33% of children in developing countries are malnourished. One hundred and fifty million are underweight, and 175 million are unable to grow because of illness and poor nutrition.[2]

Childhood obesity is also related to poor nutrition. Over 22 million children around the world under the age of five are overweight. Eating high-fat, nutrient-poor foods and not exercising regularly lead to obesity. Long-term dangers of this type of obesity include heart disease, diabetes, and certain types of cancer.[3]

The Impacts of Poor Health

Are there ever days when you feel exhausted and you're not exactly sure why? Not eating the right nutrients or eating "empty" calories can make you feel lethargic and unfocused. Poor nutrition can make it difficult to concentrate in school and to participate in physical activities. Consuming vegetables and fruits, decreasing high amounts of sweets and salt, and reducing saturated fats and oils could make a huge impact on your ability to be at your best throughout the day.[4]

> ## "He who has health has hope, and he who has hope has everything."
> ### —Arabian proverb

Healthy Choices

Optimal health occurs through a balance of food and exercise, along with avoiding unhealthy behaviors. Try one of the following ideas and see the impact it makes on you:

- Exercise at least three to five times per week. Exercise can include walking, playing sports, or playing games that involve physical activity.
- Avoid eating excessive amounts of sugars and fats.
- Increase the amount of fruits and vegetables you eat.
- Support hunger-related causes, ranging from volunteering at local food banks and contributing to food drives to supporting hunger-related international organizations.

1 UNICEF, "Introduction," www.unicef.org/nutrition/index.html (accessed October 27, 2008).
2 UNICEF, "Nutrition, the Big Picture," www.unicef.org/nutrition/index_bigpicture.html (accessed October 27, 2008).
3 World Health Organization, "Why does childhood overweight and obesity matter?," www.who.int/dietphysicalactivity/childhood_consequences/en/index.html (accessed October 28, 2008).
4 Mayo Clinic, "Food Pyramid: An Option for Better Eating," www.mayoclinic.com/health/healthy-diet/NU00190 (accessed January 21, 2009).

Increasing the Peace,[1] page 1

Objectives

- Use double bar graphs to represent data
- Use line graphs to evaluate changes in youth violence over time
- Create a scatterplot and line of best fit to determine correlation among 2 variables
- Examine trends in violent crimes among youth
- Explore possible root causes of youth violence

Investigations

1. Create a double bar graph using the information in the following table. Make sure that years are shown on the x-axis.

Year	% female students that report being threatened or injured with a weapon	% male students that report being threatened or injured with a weapon
1993	5	18
1995	5	14
1997	4	13
1999	3	11
2001	3	10
2003	3	9
2005	3	10

2. Write a sentence explaining the trends observed in your double bar graph.

3. Use the following data to create a line graph, showing the trend in the number of serious violent crimes per 1000 students ages 12-18 in U.S. schools.

Year	Violent Crimes per 1000 Students
1992	10
1993	12
1994	13
1995	9
1996	9
1997	8
1998	9
1999	7
2000	5
2001	6
2003	6
2005	5

*Note that no data are available for 2002 and 2004.

4. What trend is emerging over time?

5. What are possible causes for the trend you observed?

Increasing the Peace, page 2

6. Use the following information to create a scatterplot.

Year	Homicides on School Grounds during School Day
1993	42
1994	42
1995	17
1996	29
1997	23
1998	35
1999	25
2000	9
2001	8
2002	2
2003	4
2004	10
2005	13
2006	4
2007	11

7. Now draw a line of best fit to show how the number of homicides on school grounds during a school day is changing over time. A line of best fit is a straight line (usually drawn using a ruler edge) that best represents the data. There are typically similar numbers of points above and below the line.

8. What pattern does the line of best fit reveal?

9. Based on the 3 graphs you have drawn, what observations can you make about how the number of violent incidents involving students has changed from the early 1990s to the mid 2000s?

Practice with Data & Graphs

A **line graph** is useful for representing data over a period of time. Multiple categories of data that occur over the same time period can be compared on the same graph, where each line represents a different category.

1. Use the following data[1] to complete the double line graph below. Data on violent crimes per 1000 students has already been graphed. Graph another line for violent crimes per 1000 people.

Year	Violent Crimes per 1000 Students	Violent Crimes per 1000 People
1992	10	48
1993	12	49
1994	13	51
1995	9	46
1996	9	42
1997	8	39
1998	9	36
1999	7	32
2000	5	27
2001	6	25
2002	no data available	23
2003	6	22
2004	no data available	21
2005	5	21

U.S. Crime Rates, 1992–2005

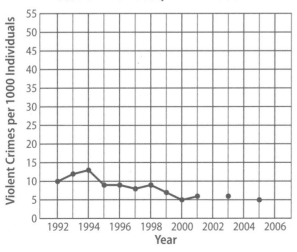

2. What trend do you observe for violent crime rates from 1992 to 2005? What are some possible causes of this trend?

3. What is 1 observation you can make about student violence versus overall violence from 1992 to 2005?

4. In 1993, 7 out of 10 local TV stories on violence in California involved youth,[2] yet youth made up only 14% of violent arrests in California that year. Why do you think the news showed so many more stories on youth violence than what was actually occurring?

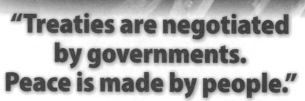

Peace and Conflict

[handwritten: Where in the world do they have the highest violence?]

[handwritten: Very Annoying]

Imagine waiting in line for lunch when suddenly someone cuts in line in front of you. What's your first reaction? Do you push the person out of line, or do you remain calm? What are the consequences of reacting?

Peace is an essential condition for maintaining a stable world and for enjoying a good quality of life. Without security and stability, other quality of life considerations such as good health and sufficient income mean little. Peace means different things to different people. What does peace look like to you?

[handwritten: # of conflicts = evidence of peace]

One definition of peace is the absence of conflict. *Conflict* describes a struggle, opposition, or disagreement. Conflict can take many forms, and not all conflicts are bad. Conflicts can lead to greater insights, communication, and resolution. However, conflicts can also take the form of violent crimes committed against individuals, wars among nations, and acts of terrorism.

Reducing Conflict

The underlying conditions of many conflicts are often the same. A global focus on addressing root causes of violence has the potential to prevent many conflicts. Some strategies include reducing poverty, providing education, encouraging good governance, supporting basic human rights, and protecting environmental resources.

Conflict by the Numbers

[handwritten: Violence is decreasing around the world]

While there are many conflicts occurring around the world, there is cause for hope. Consider the following statistics:[2]

- Fatalities from terrorism around the world have declined in recent years.
- The number of armed conflicts and related

[handwritten: Good stats]

casualties in sub-Saharan Africa has decreased dramatically over the last decade.
- The number of conflicts between communal or rebel groups has gone down worldwide during the last 5 years.
- Civilian fatalities in Iraq declined in 2007.
- In the United States violent crime rates have dropped dramatically since the early 1990s.

Peace Is an Ongoing Process

[handwritten: It's still a problem]

These positive trends do not mean that conflicts—violent and otherwise—are not a serious problem around the world. But the trends do suggest that individual actions, when combined, can change the realities we are faced with. There are many opportunities for each of us to be part of building peace.

We can become more educated about other cultures. We can work to resolve disagreements with friends and family peaceably. We can become peer mediators to help others resolve their disputes. We can also support local, national, and international efforts to prevent violence and promote peace.

---

1 Seeds of Peace is an organization that provides leadership training to young people from regions of conflict. www.seedsofpeace.org.

2 *Human Security Report Project*, Simon Fraser University, Human Security Brief 2007, www.humansecuritybrief.info (accessed January 28, 2009) and Steven D. Levitt and Stephen J. Dubner, *Freakonomics* (New York: HarperCollins Publishers Inc., 2005).

Paper or Plastic?, page 1

Objectives

- Simplify and compare fractions
- Write fractions as decimals
- Evaluate the pros and cons of different con-sumption choices

Investigations

You will use information from the following table to make an informed choice about which kind of cup you would purchase.[1]

Table 1. Background Information for Cup Types

	Cost (price/ quantity)	Weight of 1 Cup (in grams, g)	Energy Used per Cup (in megajoules, MJ)
Plastic	$11/1000	59	6.3
Styrofoam	$25/1000	1.9	0.20
Paper	$40/500	8.3	0.55
Ceramic	$20/3	292	14
Stainless Steel	$15/1	378	8.1

1. Use the information from Table 1 to complete the following table.

Table 2. Price and Reusability of Cups

	What is the price of 1 cup?	Can the cup be reused many times?
Plastic		
Styrofoam		
Paper		
Ceramic		
Stainless Steel		

2. Based on these prices, how many paper cups could you buy for the price of 1 ceramic mug?

3. Create an algebraic equation that would allow you to determine the number of plastic cups that can be produced using the same amount of energy used to produce 1 ceramic mug.

4. Use mental math to solve the equation you created in the previous problem to determine approximately how many plastic cups could be produced using the same amount of energy that it takes to produce 1 ceramic mug. Report your answer as a whole number.

Paper or Plastic?, page 2

5. How many times would you need to reuse the ceramic mug to use less total energy than getting a new plastic cup each time?

6. What other kinds of information would help you decide which cup you want to purchase?

7. List at least 1 pro and 1 con for purchasing each type of cup.

Plastic
- Pro: _____
- Con: _____

Styrofoam
- Pro: _____
- Con: _____

Paper
- Pro: _____
- Con: _____

Ceramic
- Pro: _____
- Con: _____

Stainless Steel
- Pro: _____
- Con: _____

8. Which cup would you purchase? Give reasons for your answer.

Bonus

People in the United States use 100 billion plastic bags each year, made from an estimated 12 million barrels of oil.[2] If U.S. consumers were to decrease their use of plastic bags by $\frac{1}{4}$ each year for the next 5 years, how many bags would they use in year 5?

Practice with Fractions

Fractions represent a part of a whole. For example, imagine dividing a pie into 5 equal pieces. If you eat 2 of those pieces, you have eaten $\frac{2}{5}$ of the pie.

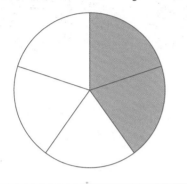

Consider the following facts:[1]

• One-third of the planet's natural resources were consumed over the course of the past 3 decades.

• 70 garbage cans of waste were produced to make the materials in a single can of garbage discarded in the United States.

• Of the 80,000 chemicals that are in the materials we buy and use, 15,000 have been tested for safety.

• Average daily water consumption per person in the United States is 425 liters per day.

1. During the past 30 years, what fraction of the planet's natural resources was used *each year?*

2. If you throw out 3 cans of garbage every 2 weeks, how many cans of waste would it take to produce 1 month's worth of your discarded materials?

3. What fraction of chemicals has been tested for safety concerns? Write your fraction in lowest terms.

4. If U.S. water usage was decreased by $\frac{1}{5}$, what would be the average water consumption per person per day?

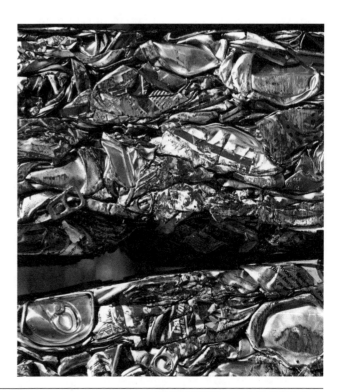

Spending Spree

Picture all the things in your home, plus the things in your neighbor's home and in your whole neighborhood. Here in the United States many of us are used to having a lot of stuff. We don't even need very much money to be able to buy a lot of things or eat as much as we want. Although we may take our luxuries for granted, things weren't always this way.

The purchase of goods and services is often called *consumption*. In the last century, world consumption multiplied 16 times, from $1.5 trillion in 1900 to $24 trillion in 1998.[1] During the same period, world population quadrupled; that means that overall consumption has increased four times as much as population. People are buying a lot more stuff!

Consumption Costs

Even in wealthier countries, the rise in consumption has not been all good or equal for everyone. According to the U.S. Environmental Protection Agency, most of what we buy ends up in landfills. Manufacturing and transporting all the things we purchase pollutes the air, water, and soil with toxic chemicals and releases greenhouse gases that contribute to climate change. Resources are being used up faster than they can renew themselves, which means we are losing many forests, natural areas, and species of plants and animals.

While the wealthiest global citizens are the main consumers, the environmental damage from this consumption falls most heavily on the poor. In both developed and developing countries, poor people are the most exposed to pollution, hazardous wastes, droughts, floods, and deforestation. For example, landfills and power plants are usually located closer to poor people than to their wealthier neighbors.

"You can't have everything... where would you put it?"
—Stephen Wright, comedian

Does This Mean We Have to Stop Consuming?

Of course not! We can continue to consume, but becoming conscious of what we buy is important. If we want a sustainable planet—one where future generations can enjoy plenty of resources and a healthy environment—we have to think about what and how we are consuming. One place to start is by not buying things we don't need, and by giving things we don't use to others who might need them. We can also buy things that are reused or recycled and make sure to reuse and recycle them when we don't want them anymore.

Whether we wear designer brands or make our own clothes, or whether we use disposable or reusable cups, all of our choices affect how sustainable the world can be. Even small changes in the things we buy can have a huge collective impact. For example, if every U.S. household replaced a single box of petroleum-based powder laundry detergent with vegetable-based detergent, 96,000 barrels of oil could be saved.[2] What are some simple choices you can make to create positive change?

1 United Nations Development Programme (UNDP), "Human Development Report 1998," http://hdr.undp.org/en/ reports/ global/hdr1998/.
2 Seventh Generation, www.seventhgeneration.com/Laundry-Detergents (accessed December 1, 2008).

Did You Budget for That?

Objectives
- Work flexibly with fractions and percents
- Understand how interest accrued over time impacts overall costs
- Evaluate the judgment of personal finance choices

Scenario 1: Jason is a senior at West High School. He works at a skateboard shop making $9 an hour. He works about 25 hours each month. He has been saving money so that he can buy a used car when he graduates.

1. If Jason works 25 hours this month and $\frac{1}{4}$ of his paycheck goes to taxes, how much money will he take home?

2. Jason takes his little brother to the movies every week, and he usually eats out at least once a week. In all, he spends about $20 each week and saves the rest of his paycheck after taxes. How much does he save each month?

3. The car Jason wants will cost him $1420. He decides that he will buy it all at once, rather than borrowing the money. For how many months will he need to save to buy it?

4. Jason has been saving money for 12 months, and he plans to work 5 more months at the skateboard store before he graduates. Do you think he has done a good job of budgeting to buy the car? Why or why not?

Scenario 2: Jadine is in ninth grade, and she does odd jobs to make money. She mows lawns, rakes leaves, walks pets, washes cars, and babysits for her neighbors. She usually charges $10 an hour for any outdoor work and $5 an hour for babysitting.

5. Jadine wants to buy a Nintendo Wii gaming system. The Wii is $300 plus 9% sales tax. How much does the Wii cost altogether, including tax?

6. Jadine has $109 in a savings account. What fraction of the Wii could her savings pay for?

7. Even though Jadine can't pay for the Wii right now, she wants to get it now so that she can play it over the weekend. She convinces her mother to put it on their family's credit card, which charges 18% interest. Jadine tells her mother that she will be able to pay back $25 each month. By paying $25 each month, she will end up paying $367.65 for the Wii. How much more will Jadine pay for the Wii by using the credit card than she would have paid if she bought it with money she had saved up?

8. Approximately how many additional hours of babysitting will Jadine need to do to pay for the Wii if it is charged to the credit card?

9. If she pays $25 each month to the credit card company, how many months will it take her to pay the entire $367.65?

10. Do you think Jadine has done a good job of budgeting to buy the Wii? Why or why not?

National Spending Spree

Objectives

- Work flexibly with fractions and percents
- Understand how nations make and spend money
- Analyze how financial choices can affect a country

Country 1
Total revenues = $2500 billion
Total expenditures = $2700 billion
Military spending = $300 billion
Education spending = $60 billion

Country 2
Total revenues = $675 billion
Total expenditures = $660 billion
Military spending = $55 billion
Education spending = $81 billion

1. What fraction of Country 1's total expenditures is made up of military spending? (Write your answer in lowest terms.)

2. Spending on health care for Country 1 amounts to $\frac{1}{10}$ of military expenditures. How much money does Country 1 spend on health care?

3. Country 1 spends more money than it takes in. How do you think this is possible?

4. What fraction of Country 2's total expenditures is made up of military spending? (Write your answer in lowest terms.)

5. Which country spends a larger fraction of its expenditures on military spending?

6. What percent of its revenues does each country budget for education?

7. Which country do you think can sustain itself for a longer period of time? Explain why in 1 sentence.

8. If you were the president of a country, would you spend a larger fraction of the budget on military, education, or health care? Why?

9. In your opinion, what are some of the most important uses of tax dollars? Name at least 2.

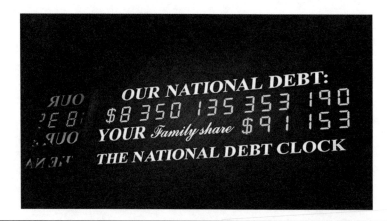

Practice with Percent

> **Percent** is a ratio that compares a number to 100. For example, $\frac{25}{100}$ is 25%.
>
> **To write a fraction as a percent**, divide the numerator by the denominator and multiply the quotient by 100. For example, the fraction $\frac{4}{5}$ can be rewritten as 80%:
>
> $$\frac{4}{5} = 0.80 \times 100 = 80\%$$
>
> **To turn a percent into a fraction**, remove the percent sign (%). The resulting number is the numerator, and 100 is the denominator. For example, 50% can be rewritten as $\frac{1}{2}$:
>
> $$50\% = \frac{50}{100} = \frac{1}{2}$$

1. Charles makes $7.25 per hour. He works after school Monday-Friday from 4-6 PM and on Saturday and Sunday from 10-3 PM. He puts 10% of every paycheck toward savings for college.

   a. How much money does Charles earn each week?

   b. How much does Charles save each week for college?

   c. Based on your last answer, calculate how much Charles saves in 1 year for college.

   d. If Charles is planning to save the rest of his earnings each week so that he can buy a new laptop for $1500, how many weeks will it take him to save enough money?

2. If 17 million U.S. students are in college and 75% own at least 1 credit card,[1] how many students around the country own a credit card?

3. One in 20 households in America owes $8,000 or more in credit card debt.[2] What is the percentage of households that owe more than $8,000 in credit card debt?

4. Country Z's expenditures are approximately 30 billion dollars.

   a. If country Z spends 3.5% of its expenditures on education, how much has it spent?

   b. Country Z spends 9 billion dollars on universal health care. Approximately what percent of country Z's expenditures does it spend on health care?

[handwritten: Why should the person's credit past affect their current decisions]

Something for Nothing?

[handwritten: It means buy now pay later]

Have you ever seen or heard an advertisement for something that could be purchased with no money down? Ever wonder what that really means? Credit cards and loans give people a chance to "buy now and pay later." Some purchases like houses and cars are so large that it's extremely difficult to pay for them all at once; often people purchase them by borrowing money. In order to borrow the money, they agree to pay interest. *Interest* is the fee that a borrower pays a lender in order to obtain a loan.

Individual Spending

At the age of 18, people can begin using credit to purchase items that they want. The advantages of credit card use could be developing a strong credit history (which allows you to make important purchases in the future) and making easy payments for big purchases. However, credit card users who are unable to pay off their debts quickly can find it difficult to borrow money in the future.

[handwritten: affects you]

By the end of 2003, over 1.3 billion credit cards were in circulation around the United States.[1] That's over 4 credit cards for every man, woman, and child in the country! Due to increased costs of living and unemployment, many people are relying on credit cards to purchase basic items such as groceries and gas.[2]

[handwritten: 4 cards per person]

National Spending

Just as an individual makes choices about how to spend money, nations also make spending choices. Much of the money they spend comes from taxes paid by citizens. If nations need to borrow money to support certain sectors of society, including education and the military, they may receive loans from other countries or businesses.

"No man's credit is as good as his money."
—John Dewey, educational reformer

In October of 2008, the International Monetary Fund (IMF), the world's central organization that provides advice and financing to over 184 different countries around the world, stated that it would provide loans of up to $100 billion to countries affected by the financial global crisis that started in the United States.[3] In the past, many of these loans have come with increased interest rates if not paid back. How might higher interest rates affect a country's ability to invest in things like expanding education and improving health care?

[handwritten: loans up to $100 bill]

Start Now

Start making financial choices today that will provide you with greater opportunities in the future:

- Evaluate your spending patterns for one month. Can you afford what you buy? If you borrow money, do you pay it back quickly?
- Sit down with your family and examine your family's monthly spending patterns. What are ways in which you can all save money so that no one is developing poor credit?
- Instead of borrowing the money to buy something instantly, create a budget for yourself and raise the money you need to buy the item later.

1 Niall McKay, "Paying with Plastic: How it Works in the Rest of the World", *Frontline,* November 23, 2004, www.pbs.org/wgbh/pages/frontline/shows/credit/more/world.html.
2 Kathy Chu, "More Americans using credit cards to stay afloat," *USA Today,* March 30, 2008, www.usatoday.com/money/perfi/credit/2008-02-28-credit-cards_N.htm.
3 Mark Landler, "Healthy Countries to Receive I.M.F. Loans," *New York Times,* October 29, 2008, www.ny-times.com/2008/10/30/business/worldbusiness/30global.html?partner=rssnyt&emc=rss.

Live Long and Prosper, page 1

Objectives

- Calculate percent change in life expectancies
- Use a scatterplot and line of best fit to evaluate data
- Correlate indicators of well-being with life expectancy for a country
- Understand the concept of probability
- Investigate global trends in health and life expectancy

Investigations

1. **Percent change** gives you an idea of how much an amount has increased or decreased. For each country in the following table, calculate the percent change in life expectancy from 1960 to 2000.

2. Check for validity of answers. If life expectancy decreased from 1960 to 2000, percent change in life expectancy should be a negative number (percent decrease). If life expectancy increased, percent change should be positive (percent increase).

3. What does percent change in life expectancy tell you?

4. Which countries experienced a percent decrease, or a negative percent change, in life expectancy?

5. Give 2 possible reasons why life expectancy might decrease in a given country.

Country	Gross National Income per capita[1]	Health Expenditure per capita[2]	Percent of Population Ages 15-49 with HIV/AIDS[3]	Life Expectancy 1960[4]	Life Expectancy 2000	Percent Change in Life Expectancy
Cambodia	2920	84	0.6	42.59	53.81	+11.22
Canada	34,610	2199	0.3	71.11	78.92	+7.81
Chad	1230	25	3.5	34.86	48.47	+13.61
China	7730	104	0.1	36.31	70.25	+33.94
Jamaica	4030	162	1.5	64.37	75.34	+10.97
Kenya	1300	79	6.1	44.95	46.97	+2.02
Mexico	11,330	354	0.3	57.33	72.96	+15.68
Nepal	1630	51	0.5	38.51	58.85	+20.34
Peru	6070	246	0.6	47.97	69.31	+21.34
Sri Lanka	5000	92	<0.1	60.14	73.14	+13
Swaziland	5170	159	25.9	40.39	45.62	+5.23
Thailand	9140	321	1.4	52.64	68.81	+16.17
Ukraine	7510	219	1.4	69.32	68.28	−0.a4
United States	44,260	3829	0.6	69.77	77.06	+7.29
Venezuela	7440	241	0.7	59.82	73.34	+13.52
Zambia	1000	39	17.0	41.78	37.97	−3.81

Live Long and Prosper, page 2

3·separate graphs

6. Investigate 1 of the other statistics listed (GNI per capita, Health Expenditure per capita, or Percent of Population Ages 15-49 with HIV/AIDS) to see if there is a correlation between that statistic and life expectancy in the year 2000. To determine whether a correlation exists, create a scatterplot. For each country, designate your chosen variable as x, and Life Expectancy as y. Thus, each country will have one ordered pair (x, y) for a total of 16 points on the graph.

7. For the scatterplot you created, would it matter if life expectancy was on the y-axis rather than the x-axis?

8. Write 1 sentence to describe the relationship between the 2 variables in your scatterplot.

9. Draw a line of best fit on your scatterplot.

10. Suppose a child born in Ethiopia in 1980 had a 70% probability of living until the age of 40. Does this mean the child will definitely live until at least the age of 28?

Bonus

Especially in wealthier countries, obesity can lower life expectancy. Obesity is related to health problems such as diabetes, high blood pressure, and poor sleep. In the United States, 37% of adult males and 42% of adult females are obese.[5] If the population of the United States is approximately 300 million, and 50% of the population of male, what is the number of men who are obese?

Practice with Rates, Ratios, & Proportions

A **rate** represents a relationship between 2 quantities, or numbers, that have different units of measure.

Example: 8 miles per hour (8 miles, 1 hour)

A **ratio** represents a relationship between 2 quantities, or numbers, that have the same units of measure.

Example: 1 person out of 100 (1 person, 100 persons)

A **proportion** is an equation that shows how 2 ratios are equal.

Example: $\frac{1}{5} = \frac{2}{10}$

To solve a proportion for an unknown variable (*x*), use inverse operations or multiply cross products.

Inverse Operations

$$\frac{x}{4} = \frac{3}{12}$$
$$4(\tfrac{x}{4}) = 4(\tfrac{3}{12})$$
$$x = \frac{12}{12}$$
$$x = 1$$

Multiply Cross Products

$$\frac{x}{4} = \frac{3}{12}$$
$$3 \cdot 4 = x \cdot 12$$
$$12 = 12x$$
$$\frac{12}{12} = \frac{12x}{12}$$
$$1 = x$$

---

1. Label each of the following scenarios as a rate or ratio.

   a. _____ Gross National Income (measured in dollars) per person

   b. _____ Number of people living with HIV out of 100 people

   c. _____ Dollars spent on books versus dollars spent on food

   d. _____ Three meals/day

2. Write a **ratio**, in simplest terms, to represent the following scenario:

   In the United States, 48 children out of 300 children are obese (weigh over 20% more than their ideal body weight).[1]

3. Write a **rate** to represent the following scenario:

   Each year in the United States, individuals with diabetes spend an average of $12,000 on health care.[2]

4. Set up and solve the following **proportion**:

   If 85 babies out of 100 births survive to adulthood, how many babies out of 1500 births will survive to adulthood?

A Global Checkup

What does good health mean to you? Many people think of health as the absence of illness. A broader definition of health is provided by the World Health Organization (WHO), which defines it as a state of complete physical, mental, and social well-being.

Being healthy is something that everyone around the world cares about. Without good health, other desirable aspects of a decent quality of life—sufficient income, a good education, and time spent with friends and family—are worth little.

Advances in medicine in the past fifty years have meant that more people around the world are surviving past childhood and the average life span is increasing. In fact, this has been one of the major reasons for population growth in recent times. Yet many people struggle to meet the most basic human needs of food, water, shelter, and personal safety. A lack of these basic needs can lead to malnutrition and can leave people more vulnerable to diseases.

Life expectancy (the number of years a newborn is expected to live) is significantly lower in the world's poorer countries than it is in wealthier countries. It is especially the women and children in poorer countries that suffer from illness and disease.

AIDS: A Global Health Challenge

One disease that has spread to all types of people in all corners of the globe is AIDS. Human Immunodeficiency Virus (HIV) is the virus that causes AIDS, a condition that includes symptoms such as infections and cancers. According to the WHO, an estimated 33 million people worldwide live with HIV/AIDS. In the United States alone, over 1 million Americans have HIV/AIDS.[1]

Most health experts agree that this epidemic is the greatest threat to world health in terms of its proven potential for spreading. As WHO Director-General Dr. Margaret Chan said, "AIDS is the most challenging and probably the most devastating infectious disease humanity has ever had to face."[2] Although HIV/AIDS has reduced the average life span in some regions of the world, especially in sub-Saharan Africa, people throughout the world are attempting to limit AIDS through education about how to prevent the spread of HIV.

"My patients in Haiti can now vote but they can't get medical care or clean water."

—Dr. Paul Farmer, medical anthropologist and physician

Educate Yourself

As it turns out, education has everything to do with health! There are examples all over the world of how educating women leads to healthier children and families. Some researchers have also found that people who stay in school longer enjoy longer lives and better health during old age than people with less education.[3]

You can help support local and global health through these actions:

- Visit www.nothingbutnets.net, an organization working to combat malaria in Africa, to learn how you can support this cause.
- Organize a Walk for Health day at school to raise money for a charity dedicated to health issues.
- Educate yourself and others about local and global health issues.

1 CDC, "HIV/AIDS in the United States," www.cdc.gov/hiv/resources/factsheets/us.htm (accessed August 1, 2008).
2 Dr. Margaret Chan, "Message for World AIDS Day," December 1, 2008, www.who.int/mediacentre/news/statements/ 2008/s13/en/index.html.
3 Gina Kolata, "A Surprising Secret to a Long Life: Stay in School," The New York Times, January 3, 2007.

Budgeting for Climate Change, page 1

Objectives

- Graph an inequality on a number line
- Solve inequalities using multiplication and division
- Work with decimals
- Recognize that daily activities release CO_2 and other greenhouse gases
- Investigate actions to reduce our contributions to climate change

Investigations

1. One way that we contribute to climate change is by doing things that release CO_2 into the air. The Kyoto Protocol is an agreement among nations that sets a target for maximum CO_2 emissions for each nation. The U.S. emissions target is 24.80 pounds per person per day.[1]

   Graph the following inequality on a number line: $x \leq 24.80$

2. Using information from the following table, write an inequality that would allow you to calculate the number of miles you can drive in an average car and remain below 24.80 pounds of CO_2. Use the variable m to represent number of miles.

CO_2 Emissions per Activity

Activity	Emissions (lbs)
Drive 1 mile in an average car	1.10 *
Drive 1 mile in a SUV	1.67 *
Eat 1 cheeseburger	6.78 **
Eat 1 PB&J sandwich	2.50 ***
Read and throw away a newspaper	0.50 ****
Use and throw away an aluminum can	0.45 ****
Take hot shower for 1 minute	1.10 *****
Leave appliances plugged in when not in use	0.27 *****

3. Now solve the inequality you wrote for question #2 to determine the number of miles you could drive in a day without exceeding 24.80 pounds of CO_2 emissions.

4. Do you think it would be easy or difficult for most people to drive less than that number of miles on a daily basis? Why or why not?

5. How could people travel without using cars?

6. The following equation allows us to determine how many miles a person can drive in a day and how many 5-minute showers a person can take and still remain below 24.8 pounds of CO_2 emissions.

$$5.5s + 1.1m \le 24.8$$

If you take 2 showers (that is, $s = 2$), what is the maximum number of miles you can drive?

7. Approximately how many PB&J sandwiches could you eat before you created more emissions than 1 cheeseburger?

8. If you throw away newspapers, throw away aluminum cans, and leave appliances plugged in when you are not using them, how many emissions would be produced from those activities in a single day?

9. Approximately what fraction of the maximum CO_2 emissions (24.8) is represented by the total emissions from question #8?

Hint: Round each number to the nearest whole number.

Bonus

The annual carbon footprint of the average person living in the United States—20.4 tons of CO_2—is around 2,000 times that of someone living in the African nation of Chad.[2]

What is the annual carbon footprint (in pounds of CO_2) of the average person living in Chad?

What is the minimum number of individual carbon footprints in Chad that would be required to exceed the average CO_2 emissions of 1 person in the U.S.?

Practice with Inequalities

There are 4 inequality symbols to remember:

$x < 5$ means x is a number *less than* 5

$x \leq 5$ means x is a number *less than or equal to* 5

$x > 5$ means x is a number *greater than* 5

$x \geq 5$ means x is a number *greater than or equal to* 5

Solving an inequality using **addition** or **subtraction** is similar to solving an equation. Any operation (addition or subtraction) that you do on one side of the inequality must also be done on the other side.

$$x + 5 < 20$$
$$ -5 \quad -5$$
$$x < 15$$

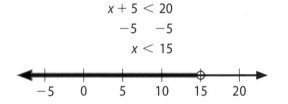

If you **multiply** or **divide** both sides of an inequality by a positive number, the inequality sign remains unchanged.

$$\frac{3x}{3} \geq \frac{27}{3}$$
$$x \geq 9$$

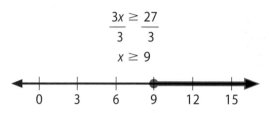

When you multiply or divide both sides of an inequality by a **negative** number, the inequality symbol reverses.

$$-2x + 5 > 25$$
$$ -5 \quad -5$$
$$\frac{-2x}{-2} > \frac{20}{-2}$$
$$x < -10$$

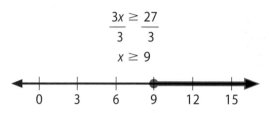

1. Suppose a person uses *nearly* 3,000 more kilowatt-hours of electricity in a year than the average American household. If the average American household uses 10,656 kilowatt-hours of electricity,[1] solve the following inequality to find that person's electricity usage: $x - 3,000 < 10,656$

2. Write a sentence explaining your answer for problem #1.

3. Suppose a city institutes a water restriction to conserve fresh water resources during hot summer months. The city will allow each resident to consume *no more than* 85 gallons of water per person per day. Write an inequality to represent this scenario.

Solve the following inequalities for x. Graph each solution on a number line.

4. $\left(-\frac{1}{3}\right)x > 30$

5. $-3 + 5x > 25$

6. $25 \leq -x$

Is there a way to produce energy without releasing greenhouse gases?

CO₂ causes global warming

Carbon, Carbon Everywhere!

CO₂ emissions are called footprints

We know that greenhouse gas emissions such as carbon dioxide are a major contributor to climate change. So how can we evaluate our contributions to climate change and greenhouse gas emissions?

A carbon footprint is one way to measure your impact on the climate. It gives you an idea of the amount of greenhouse gases your activities produce. It is often measured in pounds of carbon dioxide (CO_2) emissions. We call it a footprint because it's like the mark you leave on the earth as you go about your daily activities. When you walk on a sandy beach, you leave behind a footprint. When you do an activity or use an item that produces greenhouse gases, you leave behind a carbon footprint.

Parts of a Footprint

Two major components of your footprint are electricity and transportation. We need energy for all of our daily activities, but electricity and transportation require the largest amounts of energy.

Think about a few of the things you do every morning. You may turn off your alarm clock, turn on a lamp, or take a hot shower. All of those things require electricity. In many places, our electricity comes from burning fossil fuels such as coal, natural gas, propane, or heating oil. When they are burned to produce energy, fossil fuels emit greenhouse gases. Greenhouse gases like carbon dioxide warm the planet and are released every time we use electricity that was created by burning fossil fuels. This warming is dangerous and could lead to severe flooding, biodiversity loss, glacial melting, and other serious consequences.[1]

fossil fuels release gases

Many of our daily activities also require transportation. You might ride in a car or bus to get to school. That requires petroleum oil, a fossil fuel used to make gasoline and diesel. Most of the things we buy also require transportation at various stages, including transportation of raw materials to a factory and transportation of finished goods to a store.

As you're beginning to see, greenhouse gases are emitted all the time! By becoming aware of the impacts of your daily activities, you can better choose how large or small your carbon footprint will be.

"The future depends on what we do in the present."
—Mahatma Gandhi, former political and spiritual leader of India

Shrinking Your Footprint

Here are some simple ways to reduce your carbon emissions:

- Turn off lights, appliances, and electronics when you're not using them.
- Travel on foot, by bicycle, or on public transportation when you can.
- Eat fewer processed foods and less meat.
- Buy used items instead of new.
- Recycle aluminum cans, plastic bottles, and paper.
- Plant trees and other plants that absorb CO_2.

Shrinking your carbon footprint doesn't need to be painful—you're not just giving things up, you're getting a lot, too. By helping to stop climate change, you are working to improve the quality of life for yourself and for the world!

---

1 Science Daily, "Even if Greenhouse Gas Emissions Hold Steady, Warmer World Faces Loss of Biodiversity, Glaciers," September 17, 2008, www.sciencedaily.com/releases/2008/09/080917145509.htm.

What's Your Angle?, page 1

Objectives

- Determine missing angle measurements of a triangle
- Classify angles and triangles as acute, obtuse, or right
- Identify supplementary angles
- Use the Pythagorean theorem to calculate the length of a missing side of a right triangle
- Use trigonometric ratios to determine the length of a missing side of a triangle
- Explore solar power as a form of renewable energy

Investigations

1. What kinds of places do you think would be best for using solar energy (energy from the sun)?

2. Solar panels consist of photovoltaic cells, which are devices that turn the sun's energy into electricity. In order to get the most energy from the sun that you possibly can, you need to position solar panels at a particular angle. The goal is for the sun to hit the panel perpendicularly.

To calculate the optimal angle at which to tilt your solar panel from the horizon, multiply your latitude by 0.9 and add 29 degrees.[1] Find the optimum angle of tilt for the following latitudes, using the formula just given.

Latitude	Angle
5°	33.5°
20°	
35°	
50°	
65°	

3. The following solar panel is to be installed at 35° latitude using a pole mount. The configuration looks like the following drawing. Angle B is the angle that you calculated for 35° latitude. Find the measure of Angle A.

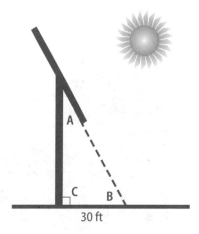

30 ft

4. Is m∠B acute, right, or obtuse?

5. What angle measurement is the supplement to ∠B?

What's Your Angle?, page 2

6. Is △ABC acute, right, or obtuse?

7. If this solar panel was to be installed at 65° latitude, would that make m∠A larger or smaller than it was in problem #3?

8. Why do you think solar panels in the Northern Hemisphere are oriented to face south?

9. Use a trigonometric ratio to find the height of the pole from ∠B. Round your answer, in degrees, to the nearest tenths place.

10. Use the Pythagorean theorem to find the hypotenuse of △ABC. Round your answer, in feet, to the nearest tenth.

Bonus

How do you think the angle for tilting a solar panel from the horizon changes in summer months?

Practice with Angles

Latitude refers to the angular distance from the equator to a particular location in the world. Lines of latitude run parallel to the equator.

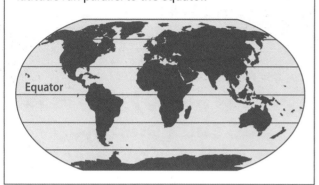

Equator

1. Below are latitudes (measured in degrees) of 12 cities. The solar energy used to power solar panels (which produce electricity) is best found at midday when the sun is the strongest. Calculate the angle for tilting a solar panel from the horizon that allows the most solar energy to be captured by a solar panel. To calculate this angle for any latitude, multiply the latitude by 0.9 and add 29 degrees.[1]

Latitude (Cities)	Angle of Solar Panel Tilt
25° (Key West and Taipei)	
30° (Houston and Cairo)	
35° (Albuquerque and Tokyo)	
40° (Denver and Madrid)	
45° (Minneapolis and Milan)	
50° (Winnipeg and Prague)	

2. Why do you think the tilt angle is smaller near the equator (at Key West and Taipei)?

3. What angle measurement is complementary to the tilt angle for Winnipeg, Canada?

4. Calculate the angle from the horizon at which each of the following solar panels is mounted:

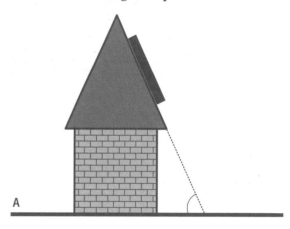

A

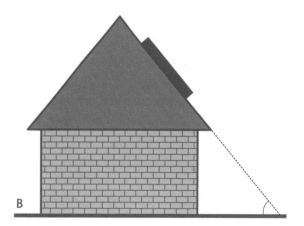

B

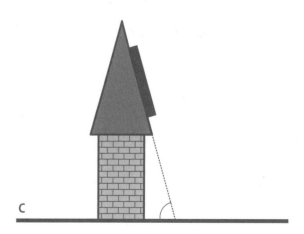

C

5. Which angle from the previous problem is near the same latitude as Winnipeg?

Are there "better energy"?

Energy and Sustainability

Energy is needed all of it

E nergy is required for everything we do. In fact, you are using energy right now! We need energy to cook, to heat our homes, and to travel from place to place. By learning about the resources required for different types of energy use and the impacts of using these resources, we can investigate the sustainability of our energy use. That is, we can determine how our energy use affects the ability of others to meet their energy needs now and into the future.

Sun is not renewable

Energy sources, or fuels, are often categorized as renewable or nonrenewable. Renewable sources can provide us with energy indefinitely. For example, wind energy is a *renewable* resource because it is continually created. Coal, on the other hand, is a *nonrenewable* resource because it can take millions of years for new coal to be produced.

Nonrenewable Energy Sources

Need to burn fossil fuels

Much of our electricity comes from burning fossil fuels. Fossil fuels, such as coal and petroleum oil, are sources of large amounts of energy. These fuels were produced by the decomposition of prehistoric plants and animals over millions of years. Any fossil fuels we use will not be replaced in our lifetime. Burning fossil fuels has negative environmental impacts, such as acid rain and smog. Burning fossil fuels has also been found to contribute to climate change.

Spotlight on Solar

Solar energy

Solar energy is renewable energy from the sun that can be converted into electrical energy. Often photovoltaic (PV) cells, which are made of metals and silicon, are used to convert solar energy into electricity. PV cells can be found on space shuttles, in watches, and on homes and office buildings.

"I'd put my money on the sun and solar energy. What a source of power!"
—Thomas Edison, inventor

lots of energy

Sunshine provides 1,000 watts of energy per square meter. This harnessed energy could power many of our buildings.[1] Although the sun is the source of an incredible amount of energy, it is difficult to use all of its energy because it is not concentrated into a single beam.

You Have the Power!

We can all reduce our impact on the earth by using sustainable sources of energy. One way to promote renewable energy resources is to purchase "green power," or electricity generated from sustainable sources. You can contact your household's local electricity provider to inquire about purchasing green power.

Energy conservation, or using less energy, is another way that everyone can have a positive impact on the earth right now. Did you know that 5% or more of your home's electricity is "leaked" from appliances and other electronics that are turned off but still plugged in?[2] At home, turn off lights, computer equipment, and appliances when you are not using them to save energy. You'll end up saving money, too!

1 How Stuff Works, "Power of Light," www.express.howstuff-works.com/exp-solar-power.htm (accessed November 25, 2008).
2 Michael Woods, "Pulling the Plug on Electricity Leaks," *Pittsburgh Post-Gazette*, May 8, 2005.

Home Sweet Habitat, page 1

Objectives

- Use formulas to find the areas of polygons
- Transform figures on a coordinate plane
- Analyze ways in which habitat size and location might affect species

Investigations

1. Calculate the area of each of the following 3 habitats of the snow leopard. (Note that the habitats are not drawn to scale.)

a) The Bronx Zoo, where snow leopards have been living for the past century

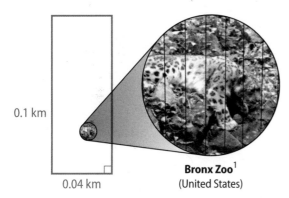

0.1 km

0.04 km

Bronx Zoo[1]
(United States)

b) Naltar Wildlife Sanctuary in Pakistan, part of the Naltar Valley where snow leopards reside

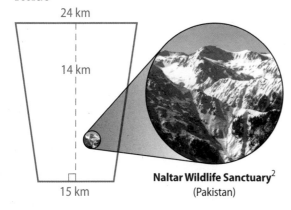

24 km

14 km

15 km

Naltar Wildlife Sanctuary[2]
(Pakistan)

c) Ajar Canyon, a wildlife reserve in Afghanistan where a few snow leopards reside

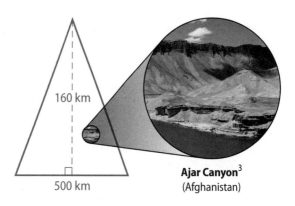

160 km

500 km

Ajar Canyon[3]
(Afghanistan)

2. What observations can you make about the relative sizes of the 3 habitats?

3. Suppose the Bronx Zoo decides to increase the snow leopard area to make it 3 times larger. What is the area of the new habitat?

4. Suppose that instead of making the zoo habitat 3 times larger, the Bronx Zoo decides to make each side of the habitat 3 times longer. Would this produce a larger or smaller habitat than your answer to #3?

5. In what ways might increasing the size of a habitat affect an animal?

6. On graph paper, graph a trapezoid with vertices E (1,1), F (16,1), G (21,15), and H (-3,15). This trapezoid represents the Naltar Wildlife Sanctuary in Pakistan.

Home Sweet Habitat, page 2

7. Developers want to build several hotels in part of the wildlife sanctuary to encourage tourism. However, a law requires that the same number of acres remain a protected wildlife refuge. To make room for the hotels but retain the same size refuge habitat, the borders of the protected region will need to move 4 km to the west and 8 km to the south. Use the formulas $x-4$ and $y-8$ to translate the vertices of your trapezoid. Draw this new trapezoid on your graph, using a different color than your original trapezoid.

8. Would it make sense to move a protected refuge from an area where snow leopards currently reside to a new area? Explain why you think it is a good idea or a bad idea.

9. Funding to maintain the protected sanctuary in Pakistan has been cut in half. The Parks Director is in charge of reducing the protected area by half. She draws the same trapezoid on graph paper that you did in problem #6, with vertices E (1,1), F (16,1), G (21,15), and H (-3,15). She decides to multiply each coordinate by $\frac{1}{2}$ in order to produce a trapezoid half the size of her original figure. Draw this new trapezoid on your graph, using a different color than your original trapezoid.

10. Was the Parks Director successful in producing a new trapezoid whose area is half the area of the original trapezoid? Explain your answer.

Bonus

A snow leopard sees an ibex (a wild mountain goat) at the top of a mountain. The ibex is one of the snow leopard's favorite foods. The height of the mountain is 8,000 feet and the base of the mountain is 12,000 feet across. The base is bisected by the mountain's highest point. If the snow leopard is at the foot of the mountain, what is the distance it will need to run in order to reach the ibex?

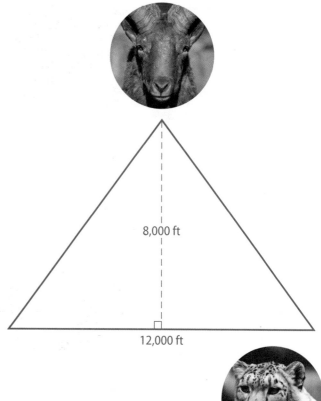

8,000 ft

12,000 ft

Practice with Transformations

A **transformation** involves the movement of a geometric figure. There are several different kinds of transformations.

One type of transformation is a **translation**, which causes a geometric figure to "slide" from one location to another. All vertices move the same distance in the same direction.

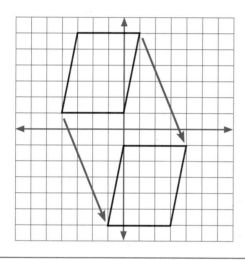

1. Describe how the *x* and *y* values in the example above change from the initial location to the new location.

2. Suppose a triangular piece of land in the Amazon Rainforest in Brazil is protected from logging. In the following coordinate plane, graph a triangle with vertices A (3, 5), B (5, 1), and C (1, 1) to represent this piece of land.

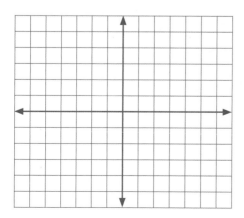

3. After the trees in the area have grown back, the triangular piece of land will be logged and a different triangular area of land to the southwest will be protected instead. Using the formulas [x − 6] and [y − 3], translate the triangle to a new area on the coordinate plane so that the triangle moves 6 units left and 3 units down. Draw this new triangular piece of protected land on the same graph, using a different color than your original square.

Another type of transformation is a **dilation**, which changes the size of a figure, not the shape.

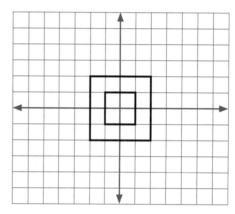

4. In the example above, both coordinates for each vertex of the larger square were multiplied by $\frac{1}{2}$ to produce the smaller square. Draw a larger figure on the same graph by multiplying each of the larger square's coordinates by 2.

Helping the Planet and Ourselves

When you walk outside your home, what living things do you encounter? Have you ever thought that many of the things you use on a daily basis come from the environment around you? The earth produces everything we need to survive, including medicinal resources, food, oxygen, and water. Ecologists and economists have calculated that if Mother Nature charged us for all the services she offered, it would amount to over $33 trillion each year![1]

It is important to understand not only how we use Earth's resources, but also the ability of the environment to supply resources over the long term. We have been using the earth in both productive and unproductive ways. If we continue to partake in unsustainable activities (such as polluting the air, destroying forests, and using up nonrenewable resources), we risk damaging the earth beyond repair.

The health of the planet relies on the health of its ecosystems, the physical environments in which all kinds of living things interact. A healthy ecosystem is often characterized by high biodiversity. *Biodiversity* refers to the variety of life in all its forms. Unfortunately, much of the world's biodiversity is disappearing.

In the past, loss of species occurred because of natural events such as temperature change. Now, humans are the main factor contributing to species extinction. Each year as many as 27,000 species of animals, plants, insects, and microorganisms disappear forever.[2] Mountain gorillas, giant pandas, and snow leopards are just a few of the more well-known animal species on the brink of extinction. Only an estimated 3,500 to 7,000 snow leopards remain in the wild.[3]

> **"In making sure that other species survive, we will be ensuring the survival of our own."**
>
> —**Wangari Maathai, 2004 Nobel Peace Prize Laureate and founder of the Green Belt Movement**

Making an Impact

Interactions between humans and our environment do not have to be negative. There are preventive measures that we can take to ensure long-term survival of the planet's resources. One example is the Golden Gate National Recreation Area in San Francisco. It is an urban national park experiment dedicated to creating a healthy ecosystem for humans, animals, plants, and the land itself. San Francisco residents work to ensure the safety of 33 endangered species in the park.[4]

What You Can Do

Here are some additional ideas for how you can have a positive impact on biodiversity:

- Buy items, including food and paper products, that were produced without destroying natural habitats.
- Plant native trees and plants in your neighborhood.
- Research all the species that exist in your area, and educate others on what you find.
- Join campaigns working to support endangered species.

1 National Environment Research Council, "Why Is Biodiversity So Important?" www.nerc.ac.uk/research/issues/ biodiversity/important.asp (accessed November 3, 2008).
2 E.O. Wilson, *The Diversity of Life* (New York: W.W. Norton & Co., 1999).
3 Snow Leopard Trust, www.snowleopard.org (accessed January 15, 2009).

Taking Shape

Objectives

- Calculate surface area and volume of cylinders and prisms
- Use geometric measurements to improve the sustainability of product design
- Investigate resource use as one consideration of sustainable design

Investigations

1. We are going to examine 2 milk container designs to see which one is more sustainable. But first, write down at least 3 ways that the concept of sustainable design could be used to redesign plastic milk jugs. **Sustainable design** *involves making products in a way that minimizes negative impacts of production on people and environmental resources while still balancing economic costs.*

2. Calculate volume for the following 2 containers:

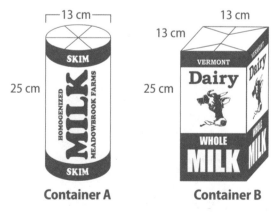

Container A   **Container B**

3. Which container holds a greater volume of milk?

4. What feature(s) of this container allows it to hold more milk?

5. How is a container's volume related to sustainable design?

6. Now calculate and compare the surface area of the 2 containers. Round answers to 2 decimal places (the hundredths place).

7. Which container has a greater surface area?

8. How is surface area related to sustainable design?

9. Of the 2 containers, which one would you recommend stores carry? Take into consideration volume, surface area, production and transport costs, the environment, and usability.

10. What other design features would you add to the preferred container to make it even easier to use? Explain how these features would affect the sustainability of the container's design, either positively or negatively.

Practice with Surface Area & Volume

Surface area is the sum of the areas of the faces or surfaces of a 3-dimensional object.

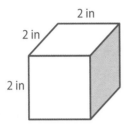

The area of any side of the above cube is 4 in². (2 in × 2 in = 4 in²)

In the case of a cube, all 6 sides have the same area.

The surface area can be found by adding together the areas of all sides:

4 in² + 4 in² + 4 in² + 4 in² + 4 in² + 4 in² = 24 in²

Volume is the number of cubic units (such as cm³) that are needed to fill a 3-dimensional figure.

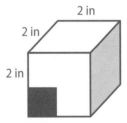

For a cube or prism, the volume (V) is the base area (B) multiplied by the height (h).

In this example, B = 2 in × 2 in = 4 in².

V = Bh = 4 in² × 2 in = 8 in³

That means that 8 cubic inches can fit inside the cube.

1. Juice cartons can be recycled into notebook covers. Calculate the surface area of the following juice carton in square centimeter (cm²).

9.5 cm
9.5 cm
19 cm

NO PULP
100%
Orange
Juice

2. A company wants to make small notebooks out of juice cartons. The notebooks have front and back covers that are each 15 cm long and 10 cm wide. How many complete notebooks can be made from a single juice carton?

3. A different company wants to devise a way to recycle the juice cartons, sanitize them, and refill them. What is the maximum volume (in cubic centimeters, or cm³) of liquid that each carton can hold?

Designer Products

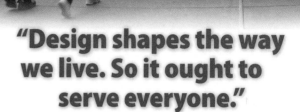

When you think of designer products, perhaps the high-end fashion styles of Gucci or Guess come to mind. Imagine instead a type of "designer product" that looks different from anything you've seen. These products take design to an entirely new level because they are designed not only to meet our practical needs, but they are also designed to minimize costs and environmental damage.

Think about the last product you purchased and ask yourself these questions: How was it designed? Do you still have it? How many different types of materials do you think it is made of? What kind of packaging did it come in? How many different places did it travel before it reached your home?

Sustainably designed products rely on the simple idea that we can create products and buildings in such a way that we minimize their negative impacts on the environment and human health while maximizing economic benefits. There are many examples of products that are made according to these principles: furniture made from fast-growing bamboo plants, clothing made from minimally processed merino wool, coffee harvested by people who are paid a fair wage, and buildings that maximize natural sunlight.

Closing the Loop

Can you guess what raw materials are used to make a DVD? It takes many types of materials to make a single DVD, including aluminum, gold, dye, water, glass, silver, nickel, and plastic made from petroleum oil.[1] Each of these materials must be extracted from the earth and manufactured into a useful product. Some of the resources are not renewable. If we constantly use nonrenewable resources to create products, we risk running out

> ## "Design shapes the way we live. So it ought to serve everyone."
> —**Eva Maddox, interior architect and designer, co-founder of Archeworks**

of these precious materials. At the end of a DVD's useful life, the owner must decide what to do with it—throw it away, recycle it, or get creative and recycle it as a sun catcher or drink coaster.

Manufacturing products like DVDs with sustainability in mind may require rethinking how they are made. Using sustainable design concepts means thinking not only about what kinds of resources are used to make a product but also what will happen to that product at the end of its life. Products inspired by "cradle to cradle" design principles are created from materials that can be perpetually recycled. The idea is not to simply minimize use of harmful materials but to maximize use of materials that can be used infinitely, whether to become part of a new product or to become nutrients for a garden.[2]

The next time you want to buy something, think about whether it is a 'designer product' for the future. Does it use renewable resources? Does it use the most efficient amount of space? Does it positively contribute to the environment, to people, and to the economy? If not, try to find an alternative that does. Our everyday choices can have a big impact, especially when we work together.

1 U.S. Environmental Protection Agency, "The Life Cycle of a CD or DVD," Solid Waste and Emergency Response educational poster, April 2003, www.epa.gov/osw.
2 McDonough Braungart Design Chemistry, "Transforming Industry: Cradle to Cradle Design," www.mbdc.com (accessed November 21, 2008).

Bears in the Air

Objectives
- Graph a function
- Calculate slope
- Use systems thinking to look at problems

Investigations

1. In the chart below, fill in the time it took you to complete each trial:

Trial (x)	Time, in Seconds (y)
1	
2	
3	
4	
5	
6	
7	
8	
9	
10	

2. Plot points from Trial 1 and Trial 2 on a coordinate plane.

3. Calculate the slope of the line formed by these 2 points.

4. Based on the slope you just calculated, what would the time of the 8th trial be, assuming your progress proceeds linearly?

5. Plot points for the remaining trial results on the same graph where you plotted Trials 1 and 2.

6. How does the actual time recorded for Trial 8 compare to the time you estimated based on slope (problem #4)? If they are different, why do you think they are different?

7. Do you think there is a limit to how fast you could complete the tossing activity? Why, or why not?

Making the Grade

Objectives

- Graph linear functions
- Calculate slope
- Use systems thinking to look at problems

Assigned Region: _____

Investigations

You will be investigating trends in primary education (grades K-8) for a certain region in the world.

The United Nations has developed **Millennium Development Goals** to reduce extreme poverty. One of the goals is to achieve universal primary education, meaning every child in the world is able to complete primary school.

The chart below shows the target percentages of primary school completion in 4 regions around the world—if the Millennium Development Goal on education is to be achieved by 2015.[1]

	2000	2005	2010	2015
Africa	54%	70%	78%	92%
South Asia	71%	83%	90%	94%
Latin America / Caribbean	76%	82%	88%	92%
Europe/Central Asia	92%	94%	96%	98%

1. Create a line graph in blue representing your assigned region's projected percentages from 2000 to 2015.

2. Does your graph indicate a linear increase in the region's percentages over a given time? How do you know whether the data you graphed indicate a linear trend or not?

3. Here are the estimated percentages of primary school completion, based on completion rates in the 1990s:

	2000	2005	2010	2015
Africa	54%	56%	58%	
South Asia	71%	74%	77%	
Latin America / Caribbean	75%	74%	73%	
Europe/Central Asia	92%	93%	94%	

On the same graph where you charted your specific region's targets for achieving 100% primary school completion by 2015, graph the completion rates for your region from the second table with a red pen.

4. Explain in 1 sentence what the 2 lines on your graph indicate.

5. Using the data from the table in #3, estimate what percentage of students will complete primary school in your region by the year 2015 and write this number in the last column of the table.

6. In order to meet the goal of 100% primary school completion, does the education system in your region need a redesign? Explain your thinking.

7. The percentage of students in the United States who complete primary school is 94%.[2] How does that percentage compare to the estimated percentage of students in your region who will complete primary school in 2010?

Bonus

Based on the actual trends observed (shown in the second data table), by what year would 100% of students from each region complete primary school?

Practice with Linear Functions

> A **linear function** follows the form, $y = mx + b$.
>
> m is the **slope** of the line (a number that indicates how steeply a line goes up or down)
>
> b is the **y-intercept** (the point where the line crosses the y-axis)

1. A community wants to increase the percentage of students graduating from high school. They decide to hire more school counselors to assist high school students. The community's progress toward their goal can be described by the following function:

$y = 4x + 67$, where x is the number of new counselors hired and y is the percent of seniors who graduate each year

Complete the following table using the function $y = 4x + 67$:

x	y
1	
2	
3	
4	
5	

2. How many new counselors would need to be added to ensure that 99% of seniors graduate?

3. Graph the linear function.

4. What is the percent of seniors that will graduate if no new counselors are hired? (Note: this is the y-intercept.)

5. What is the slope of the function? Explain the function's slope in the context of counselors and graduation rates

Education for All?

W hat are the first few words that come to mind when you think about school? Are they positive, negative, or a combination of both? Consider this fact: approximately 80 million children around the world are unable to attend school.[1] When students are not able to go to school, what choices do they have for their future?

In 1948, the United Nations declared that all children have the basic right to attend school.[2] So why aren't all kids in school? Unfortunately, a number of barriers get in the way. Health, poverty, geographic distance, gender, child labor, and armed conflict are just a few of these barriers. For example, the violent conflict that has been going on for several years in Darfur, Sudan, has made it difficult for many children to complete their schooling.

Lack of a proper education can lead to a number of problems for individuals and nations. If the majority of a population does not have basic skills like reading and writing, the future of a country can suffer. However, as more and more people gain access to education, they will become empowered to build healthy, sustainable societies.

Often those who do not attend school are girls. Giving girls just one extra year of education increases living wages and decreases infant mortality.[3] In other words, a community's economy and the health of its citizens tend to improve in communities where females attend school.

Progress in Bolivia

Bolivia is one country that has made a huge transformation in education for all. After a law passed in 1994, country leaders made a decision to reform education and ensure that all children throughout the country had access to a quality education. Changes were made such as paying teachers more,

"Education is the most powerful weapon which you can use to change the world."

—Nelson Mandela, the first democratically-elected President of South Africa

creating incentives for families to send their children to school, and creating lessons in the native languages of many students. Drop-out rates decreased, sixth-grade promotion rates increased, and literacy rates for both men and women increased over a 10-year period.[4]

What Can You Do?

Governments can make an impact in ensuring education for all, and so can students like you. Here are a few ways that you can advocate for children's education around the world:

- Participate in the Global Campaign for Education's "World's Biggest Lesson" in April to promote universal education. Visit: www.campaignforeducationusa.org.
- Raise money and awareness around universal education. Donate your money and time to an organization working toward this goal.
- Finish your education so that when you grow up, you can have the choices you deserve in life and become an advocate for others to have improved educational opportunities.

1 UNICEF, "State of the World's Children 2008," www.unicef.org (accessed December 1, 2008).
2 Net Aid, "Access to Education," www.netaid.org (accessed December 1, 2008).
3 United Nations World Food Programme (WFP), "Educating Girls: The Wisest Social Investment of All," www.wfp.org/food_aid/ (accessed December 1, 2008).
4 Manuel E. Contreras and Maria Luisa Talavera Simoni, "The Bolivian Education Reform 1992-2002: Case Studies in Large-Scale Education Reform," November 2003, http://web.worldbank.org.

Putting Sustainability on the Map

Objectives

- Plot distances between different locations on a coordinate plane
- Use distance and midpoint formulas to analyze community resource distribution
- Determine how resource distribution affects community sustainability

Investigations

1. On a piece of graph paper, use a pencil to plot the following locations of community resources found in Greenpoint, USA, and label them to indicate the resource represented by each point.

	(x, y)
Public library	(2, 4)
Landfill	(8, 9)
Hospital	(4, 6)
Jail	(7, 1)
Airport	(4, 8)
Elementary school	(6, 7)
High school	(4, 4)

2. Use the midpoint formula to determine the midpoint between the elementary school and the high school.

3. Why might you want to find the midpoint between any 2 community resources?

4. Your community voted to build a large recreational park, and now the city government is trying to decide where it should be located. There are 2 vacant lots where it could be built. Plot the following 2 points on your graph using a red pen and label them: A (1, 8) and B (5, 1).

5. Use the distance formula to calculate the following distances (in miles) from both possible park locations to key community resources. Round your answers to 2 decimal places (the hundredths place) and record them in the following table.

Community Resource	Future Park Location A (1, 8)	Future Park Location B (5, 1)
Elementary school (6, 7)		
Jail (7, 1)		
Hospital (4, 6)		

6. Based on the distances you calculated, would you choose location A or B for the new park? Explain your answer.

7. List at least 3 resources that would make a community more environmentally, economically, or socially sustainable. Explain how each resource would impact sustainability.

8. Would it be easy or difficult for someone without a car to live in Greenpoint? Why?

9. Do you think the community where you live is sustainable? If yes, what features make it sustainable? If no, what features would improve your community?

Bonus

The midpoint between the high school and the history museum is (2, 9). What are the coordinates of the history museum?

Practice with Midpoint & Distance

The **distance formula** is used to find the distance between 2 separate points, (x_1, y_1) and (x_2, y_2).

$$d = \sqrt{(x_2 - x_1)^2 + (y_2 - y_1)^2}$$

The **midpoint formula** is used to find the midpoint of a line segment between 2 points, (x_1, y_1) and (x_2, y_2).

$$m = \left(\frac{x_1 + x_2}{2}, \frac{y_1 + y_2}{2} \right)$$

1. In Mini City, the school location is at $(1, 7)$ and the apartment building location is at $(4, 1)$. Using the distance formula, find the distance between the school and the apartment building.

2. Builders want to create a community center in between the school and the apartment building. What is the midpoint between the 2 locations?

3. Do you think this is a good location for the community center? Why or why not?

4. The founders of Mini City wanted important community buildings to be built an equal distance from Town Hall, the center of the community. Are the post office and the library equidistant from Town Hall?

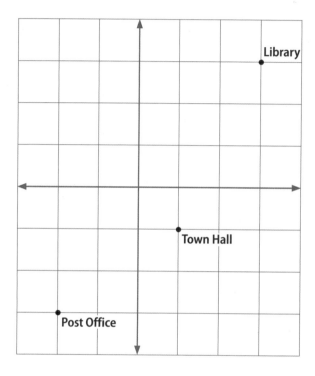

Communities That Last

Handwritten annotations:
Does the waste community needs affect how well the community is?
Grasshopper doesn't store / The story
What a community needs
Humanity community
Udaipur's / subcommunity
What ULC does

Have you heard of the fable of the grasshopper and the ant? One summer, while the grasshopper relaxed, the ant worked hard to store food for winter. When winter arrived, the ant was well prepared while the grasshopper begged for assistance. In thinking about sustainable communities, what are ways in which people can learn to prepare for the future, like the ant in the fable?

A sustainable community has economic, environmental, and social resources that residents and visitors can use to meet their basic needs now and into the future. It might include the following features: a low-cost public transportation system, a community center, a recycling program, global education in schools, energy-efficient buildings, celebration of multiple cultures, and bike lanes on streets.

Think about where you live. How is the space organized? What types of buildings and organizations surround you? Are people of all ages supported in their needs? The following examples illustrate how community resources can impact people's lives.

Across the World

The South Bronx in New York City has historically been famous for its waste processing plants and garbage dumps. An organization known as Sustainable South Bronx has worked to make the area greener and healthier. It has created a farmers market, worked to limit of the increase of power plants, and provided skills training for environmental jobs to youth.[1]

Udaipur, located in North India, is a 450-year-old city. At one point its citizens became fearful that the city would not be able to retain its rich history. They created a program called Udaipur as

> ## "We must do more to protect our neighborhoods and give integrity to our community plans."
>
> —**Alan Autry,** former mayor of Fresno, California

a Learning City (ULC). This program emphasizes the history and culture of the city. Craftspeople pass on their skills to the next generation, residents work on oral history projects, and people practice local languages so that these languages do not disappear.[2]

Creating Community

There are many ways that you can work to improve the sustainability of your neighborhood or community. Here are a few ideas to get you started:

- Evaluate your neighborhood resources. If some essential resources are missing or inadequate, petition the mayor or city council to create change.
- Create a community resource map for visitors and residents.
- Join organizations and projects that work to strengthen communities, such as youth committees, neighborhood patrols, mural projects, and community theaters.

---

1 Sarah Rich, "Urban Community Development," in *World Changing: A User's Guide for the 21st Century*, ed. Alex Steffen (Abrams, NY: Abrams, 2006): 339–341.
2 Mille Bojer, "Community Capital," in *World Changing: A User's Guide for the 21st Century*, ed. Alex Steffen (Abrams, NY: Abrams, 2006): 342–346.

The Good Life

Objectives

- Organize data using a box-and-whisker plot
- Analyze data by calculating measures of central tendency
- Compare and contrast student and adult survey responses

Investigations

1. Copy the compiled survey results into the following table:

Quality of Life Category	Student Results	Adult Results
Family		
Friends		
Health		
Rest/Relaxation		
Recreation		
Creative Pursuits		
Spiritual Pursuits		
Work/Earn Money		
Volunteer/Help Others		
The Environment		

2. Find the mean for the Student Results for the Family indicator.

3. Find the mean for the Adult Results for the Family indicator.

4. Find the median of the Student Results for the Health indicator.

5. Organize the data for the Student Results for the Health indicator in a box-and-whisker plot.

6. Write an expression representing the results in the top 25% for Student Results for the Health indicator.

7. Find the mode for the Student Results for the Recreation indicator.

8. Find the mode for the Adult Results for the Recreation indicator.

9. Based on the survey indicators, which group appears to have a higher quality of life: students or adults? Name at least 1 factor that might contribute to this group's higher scores on your survey.

Practice with Data Analysis

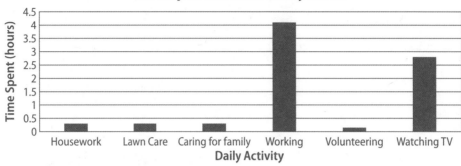

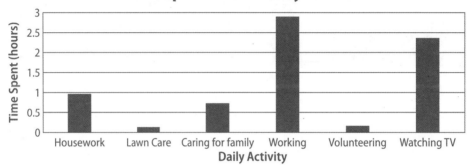

Review the above graphs of 2007 American Time Use Survey data.[1]

1. Why is it difficult to directly compare the 2 graphs shown?

2. How would you respond to someone who asked you how males and females spend their time differently?

The **mean** of a set of data can be found by adding all data together and dividing by the number of items in the data set.

The **median** of a set of data is the middle number. To find the median, you must first arrange the data in numerical order.

---

3. A group of 9 students were asked the question, "How many hours of TV do you watch each week?" Find the median of their responses:
14, 15, 13, 14, 26, 11.5, 16, 15, 12

4. What is the mean number of hours of TV watched by the 9 students above? Round your answer to 2 decimal places (the hundredths place).

5. Which measure do you think more accurately represents the data shown: mean or median? Explain your answer.

6. How would the mean be affected if you removed the student response of 26 hours?

What Do You Really Need?

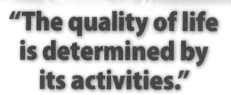

In fifty years, what will you need to have a comfortable lifestyle? When we talk about sustainability, we're talking about meeting needs—both now and into the future. Everyone has basic needs for food, water, and some form of shelter. Meeting human needs depends on a healthy environment that can continue to provide resources for us and for our children. Once their basic needs are met, people strive to meet additional needs such as creating a community of friends and finding meaningful work.

The Good Life

Quality of life refers to the well-being of an individual or group of people. It's likely that each of us has a different idea of what exactly "the good life" looks like—and it is also likely that many of us share similar ideas. What do you think the good life looks like?

For many people, happiness is one indicator of a good quality of life. Sometimes it's easy to think that we'd be a lot happier if only we had more money. This is probably true for people who are very poor and still need to meet their basic needs. But beyond a certain level of income, more money does not seem to bring more happiness. Whereas income levels doubled in the United States between 1957 and 2002, the percentage of people who reported being "very happy" did not change.[1]

The ability to buy the things we want is tied to making money, which is also tied to the amount of time people spend working. People who live in the United States tend to work long hours to buy the things they want and need, and spend a great deal of time commuting and watching television.

> ## "The quality of life is determined by its activities."
> —**Aristotle**, Greek philosopher

If increased income beyond a modest level does not guarantee a better quality of life, what does? Researchers have identified a number of key ingredients to happiness and well-being. Exercise, creativity, civic involvement, and building strong relationships with family, friends, and community often contribute to a person's happiness.

The Good News about the Good Life

The goal for improving quality of life on Earth is relatively simple: to improve well-being in a long lasting way. This goal includes maintaining a healthy economy, environment, and society for present and future generations.

How do you want to spend your time and money? What are features of a healthy society? Thinking about your answers to these questions might get you—and all of us—a little closer to the good life.

---

1 David G. Myers, "Happiness," in *Psychology, Seventh Edition* (New York: Worth Publishers, 2004).

Endnotes

Lesson 1. Number Patterns: Waste & Recycling

Lesson Handout: *Waste Not, Want Not*

1 Chris Jordan, "Running the Numbers," Chris Jordan Photography, 2008, www.chrisjordan.com/current_set2.php (accessed August 18, 2008).

2 U.S. Environmental Protection Agency (EPA), "Municipal Solid Waste Generation, Recycling, and Disposal in the United States: Facts and Figures for 2006," 2006, www.epa.gov/osw/nonhaz/municipal/pubs/msw06.pdf.

3 U.S. EPA 2006.

4 "Fun Facts About PET," www.napcor.com/plastic/bottles/funfacts.html (accessed January 27, 2009).

5 U.S. EPA 2006.

6 Ibid.

Background Reading: *What's the Big Deal?*

1 Estimates made using the Environmental Defense Fund Paper Calculator, www.papercalculator.org.

2 Natural Resources Defense Council, "Too Good to Throw Away," February 1997, www.nrdc.org/cities/recycling/ recyc/recyinx.asp.

3 Elizabeth Royte, *Garbage Land: On the Secret Trail of Trash* (New York: Little, Brown and Company, 2005), 275.

4 Ibid., 57.

5 U.S. Environmental Protection Agency, "Puzzled About Recycling's Value? Look Beyond the Bin," January 1998, www.epa.gov/osw/conserve/downloads/benefits.pdf.

Lesson 2. Introduction to Algebra: Poverty & Microcredit

Lesson Handout: *Microcredit Business Application*

1 Microcredit application adapted from Trickle Up Program Business Plan. www.trickleup.org.

Background Reading: *Poverty by the Numbers*

1 The World Bank, "Poverty Data," Supplement to *World Development Indicators 2008*, 2008, http://web.worldbank.org/WBSITE/EXTERNAL/DATASTATISTICS/0,,contentMDK:21725423~pagePK:64133150~piPK:64133175~theSitePK:239419,00.html.

2 Grameen Bank, "Grameen Bank at a Glance," www.grameen-info.org/index.php?option=com_content&task=view&id=26&Itemid=175 (accessed December 1, 2008).

3 RESULTS, "2007 Basics: Global Economic Empowerment Campaign," www.results.org/website/article.asp?id=2567 (accessed December 10, 2008).

Lesson 3. Modeling Integers: Population Growth

Lesson Handout: *The Ups and Downs of Population*

1 U.S. Census Bureau International Database, "Population Pyramid Summary for Japan", www.census.gov (accessed August 1, 2008).

2 CIA, *The World Factbook*, https://www.cia.gov/library/publications/the-world-factbook/ (accessed December 4, 2008).

3 Ibid.

Background Reading: *Increasing Numbers*

1 U.S. Census Bureau (www.census.gov), CIA *World Factbook* (https://www.cia.gov/library/publications/the-world-factbook/), and Population Reference Bureau (www.prb.org).

2 United Nations Population Fund (UNFPA), "State of World Population 2003," www.unfpa.org/swp/2003/swpmain.htm.

3 United Nations Department of Economic and Social Affairs (ESA), "World Population Prospects: The 2004 Revision," www.un.org/esa/population/publications/WPP2004/wpp2004.htm.

4 United Nations Population Fund, "The State of World Population 2001," www.unfpa.org/swp/2001/english/ch01.html.

Lesson 4. Solving Algebraic Equations: Food Choices

Lesson Handout: *You Are What You Eat*

1 All caloric value and daily values were derived from www.caloriecount.about.com.

Practice Worksheet: *Practice with Solving Equations*

1 Information from American Cancer Society's Calorie Counter, www.cancer.org/docroot/PED/content/PED_6_1x_Calorie_Calculator.asp? debugMode=false (accessed December 3, 2008).

Background Reading: *What to Eat?*

1 UNICEF, "Introduction," www.unicef.org/nutrition/index.html (accessed October 27, 2008).

2 UNICEF, "Nutrition, the Big Picture," www.unicef.org/nutrition/index_bigpicture.html (accessed October 27, 2008).

3 World Health Organization, "Why does childhood overweight and obesity matter?," www.who.int/dietphysicalactivity/childhood_consequences/en/index.html (accessed October 28, 2008).

4 Mayo Clinic, "Food Pyramid: An Option for Better Eating," www.mayoclinic.com/health/healthy-diet/NU00190 (accessed January 21, 2009).

Lesson 5. Data & Graphs: Youth Conflict

Lesson Handout: *Increasing the Peace*

1 Data from Youth Violence Project – National Statistics, "Violence in Schools," http://youthviolence.edschool.virginia.edu/violence-in-schools/national-statistics.html (accessed August 28, 2008).

Practice Worksheet: *Practice with Data & Graphs*

1 Youth Violence Project, http://youthviolence.edschool.virginia.edu/violence-in-schools/national-statistics.html, and the U.S. Department of Justice, Bureau of Justice Statistics, www.ojp.usdoj.gov/bjs/glance/tables/viortrdtab.htm (accessed January 29, 2009).

2 Lori Dorfman, "Off Balance: Youth, Race and Crime in the News," Building Blocks for Youth, April 2001, www.buildingblocksforyouth.org/media/media.html.

Background Reading: *Peace and Conflict*

1 Seeds of Peace is an organization that provides leadership training to young people from regions of conflict. www.seedsofpeace.org.

2 Human Security Report Project, Simon Fraser University, *Human Security Brief 2007*, www.humansecuritybrief.info (accessed January 28, 2009) and Steven D. Levitt and Stephen J. Dubner, *Freakonomics* (New York: HarperCollins Publishers Inc., 2005).

Lesson 6. Number Theory: Consumption Choices

Lesson Handout: *Paper or Plastic?*

1 Information derived from Martin Hocking, "Reusable vs. Disposable Cups: An Energy-Based Evaluation," *Environmental Management* 18, no. 6 (1994); Pablo Paster, "The Coffee Mug Debacle," Ask Pablo, September 11, 2006, www.askpablo.org; and Energy Information Administration, "Recycling Metals," Energy Kid's Page, www.eia.doe.gov/kids/energyfacts/saving/recycling/solidwaste/metals.html (accessed June 30, 2008).

2 Brenna Maloney and Laura Stanton, "Paper or Plastic?," *The Washington Post*, October 4, 2007.

Endnotes, *continued*

Practice Worksheet: *Practice with Fractions*

1 *The Story of Stuff,* www.storyofstuff.com, and "Resource Kit on Sustainable Consumption and Production," www.unep.org/PDF/sc/SC_resourcekit.pdf (accessed January 19, 2009).

Background Reading: *Spending Spree*

1 United Nations Development Programme (UNDP), "Human Development Report 1998," http://hdr.undp.org/en/ reports/global/hdr1998/.

2 Seventh Generation, www.seventhgeneration.com/Laundry-Detergents (accessed December 1, 2008).

Lesson 7. Rational Numbers: Financial Decisions

Practice Worksheet: *Practice with Percent*

1 Jessica Silver-Greenberg, "Majoring in Credit Card Debt," MSNBC, September 5, 2007, www.msnbc.msn.com/id/ 20607411/page/3/.

2 Liz Pulliam Weston, "The Truth about Credit Card Debt," MSN Money, http://moneycentral.msn. com/content/Banking/creditcardsmarts/P74808.asp (accessed December 12, 2008).

Background Reading: *Something for Nothing?*

1 Niall McKay, "Paying with Plastic: How it Works in the Rest of the World", *Frontline*, November 23, 2004, www.pbs.org/wgbh/pages/frontline/shows/credit/more/world.html.

2 Kathy Chu, "More Americans using credit cards to stay afloat," *USA Today*, March 30, 2008, www.usatoday.com/money/perfi/credit/2008-02-28-credit-cards_N.htm.

3 Mark Landler, "Healthy Countries to Receive I.M.F. Loans," *New York Times*, October 29, 2008, www.nytimes.com/2008/10/30/business/worldbusiness/30global.html?partner=rssnyt&emc=rss.

Lesson 8. Proportion, Percent, & Probability: Global Health

Lesson Handout: *Live Long and Prosper*

1 Gross National Income per capita is reported in 2006 U.S. dollars, adjusted for PPP (Purchasing Power Parity). Source: Population Reference Bureau, "2007 World Population Data Sheet," 2007, www.prb.org/pdf07/07WPDS_Eng. pdf (accessed January 24, 2009).

2 Health expenditure per capita is from 1995 data, reported in international PPP dollars. Source: UC Atlas of Global Inequality, http://ucatlas.ucsc.edu/ (accessed January 24, 2009).

3 Percentages are from 2005/2006 data. Source: Population Reference Bureau, "2007 World Population Data Sheet."

4 Life expectancy is reported in total years. Source: UC Atlas of Global Inequality, http://ucatlas. ucsc.edu/ (accessed January 24, 2009).

5 Percentage of adults who were obese in 2005. Source: Population Reference Bureau, "2007 World Population Data Sheet."

Practice Worksheet: *Practice with Rates, Ratios, & Proportions*

1 "Study Offers Hope for U.S. Kids' Obesity," CBS News, May 27, 2008, www.cbsnews.com/ stories/2008/05/27/health/main4130096.shtml?source=related_story.

2 "Direct and Indirect Costs of Diabetes in the United States," American Diabetes Association, www.diabetes.org/diabetes-statistics/cost-of-diabetes-in-us.jsp (accessed February 1, 2009).

Background Reading: *A Global Checkup*

CDC, "HIV/AIDS in the United States," www.cdc.gov/hiv/resources/factsheets/us.htm (accessed August 1, 2008).

2 Dr. Margaret Chan, "Message for World AIDS Day," December 1, 2008, www.who.int/ mediacentre/news/statements/ 2008/s13/en/index.html.

3 Gina Kolata, "A Surprising Secret to a Long Life: Stay in School," *The New York Times*, January 3, 2007.

Lesson 9. Solving Inequalities: Carbon Emissions

Lesson Handout: *Budgeting for Climate Change*

1 Target numbers are based on the Kyoto Protocol target of 1,252 million metric tons C and a current U.S. population of 305,000,000.

* Sightline Institute, "How Low-Carbon Can You Go: The Transportation Emissions Ranking," www.sightline.org/ maps/charts/climate-CO2byMode.

** Jamais Cascio, "The Cheeseburger Footprint," 2007, www.openthefuture.com/cheeseburger_CF.html.

*** The PB&J Campaign, www.pbjcampaign.org/numbers.

**** EPA Individual Emissions Calculator, www.epa.gov/climatechange/emissions/individual.html.

***** Action for Climate Change, www.actionforclimatechange.org.au.

2 Rachel Oliver, "Rich, Poor and Climate Change," CNN.com, February 18, 2008, http://edition.cnn.com/2008/ BUSINESS/02/17/eco.class/index/.

Practice Worksheet: *Practice with Inequalities*

1 Energy Information Administration, Energy Consumption by End Use in U.S. Households, 2001. www.eia.doe.gov/emeu/reps/enduse/er01_us_tab1.html.

Background Reading: *Carbon, Carbon Everywhere!*

1 Science Daily, "Even if Greenhouse Gas Emissions Hold Steady, Warmer World Faces Loss of Biodiversity, Glaciers," September 17, 2008, www.sciencedaily.com/releases/2008/09/080917145509.htm.

Lesson 10. Spatial Thinking: Solar Power

Lesson Handout: *What's Your Angle?*

1 Charles R. Landau, "Optimum Orientation of Solar Panels," 2002, www.macslab.com/optsolar.html.

Practice Worksheet: *Practice with Angles*

1 Charles R. Landau, 2002.

Background Reading: *Energy and Sustainability*

1 How Stuff Works, "Power of Light," www.express.howstuffworks.com/exp-solar-power.htm (accessed November 25, 2008).

2 Michael Woods, "Pulling the Plug on Electricity Leaks," *Pittsburgh Post-Gazette*, May 8, 2005.

Lesson 11. Area & Transformations: Wildlife Habitats

Lesson Handout: *Home Sweet Habitat*

1 Judy Aita, "Snow Leopard Cub Settles into U.S. Home," September 25, 2006, *America.gov*, www.america.gov/st/washfile-english/2006/September/20060925180702eaifas0.7183344.html.

2 Pakistan Paedia, "Wild Life Sanctuaries in Pakistan," www.pakistanpaedia.com/wildlife/wetlands/wild-life-sanctuaries-in_pakistan.html (accessed October 7, 2008).

3 J. M. Ledgard, "Afghanistan: The Snow Leopards and Sacred Cave of Ajar Canyon," Radio Free Europe/Radio Liberty © 2003, www.globalsecurity.org/military/library/news/2003/10/mil-031017-rferl-161744.htm (accessed October 8, 2008).

Background Reading: *Helping the Planet and Ourselves*

1 National Environment Research Council, "Why Is Biodiversity So Important?" www.nerc.ac.uk/research/issues/ biodiversity/important.asp (accessed November 3, 2008).

2 E.O. Wilson, *The Diversity of Life* (New York: W.W. Norton & Co., 1999).

3 Snow Leopard Trust, www.snowleopard.org (accessed January 15, 2009).

Endnotes, *continued*

4 Golden Gate National Recreation Area, "About the GGNRA," www.ggnrabigyear.org/about_ggnra.html (accessed January 9, 2009).

Lesson 12. Surface Area & Volume: Sustainable Design

Background Reading: *Designer Products*

1 U.S. Environmental Protection Agency, "The Life Cycle of a CD or DVD," Solid Waste and Emergency Response educational poster, April 2003, www.epa.gov/osw.

2 McDonough Braungart Design Chemistry, "Transforming Industry: Cradle to Cradle Design," www.mbdc.com (accessed November 21, 2008).

Lesson 13. Linear Functions: Global Education

Lesson Handout: *Making the Grade*

1 Data estimated from Figure 7, "Primary School Completion Progress, 1990-2015," in The State of the World's Children 2004, UNICEF, www.unicef.org/sowc04/index.html.

2 The World Bank, "Facts about Primary Education," www.worldbank.org/ieg/education/facts_figures.html (accessed January 12, 2009).

Background Reading: *Education for All?*

1 UNICEF, "State of the World's Children 2008," www.unicef.org (accessed December 1, 2008).

2 Net Aid, "Access to Education," www.netaid.org (accessed December 1, 2008).

3 United Nations World Food Programme (WFP), "Educating Girls: The Wisest Social Investment of All," www.wfp.org/food_aid/ (accessed December 1, 2008).

4 Manuel E. Contreras and Maria Luisa Talavera Simoni, "The Bolivian Education Reform 1992-2002: Case Studies in Large-Scale Education Reform," November 2003, http://web.worldbank.org.

Lesson 14. Midpoint and Distance Formulas: Resource Distribution

Background Reading: *Communities that Last*

1 Sarah Rich, "Urban Community Development," in *World Changing: A User's Guide for the 21st Century*, ed. Alex Steffen (Abrams, NY: Abrams, 2006): 339–341.

2 Mille Bojer, "Community Capital," in *World Changing: A User's Guide for the 21st Century*, ed. Alex Steffen (Abrams, NY: Abrams, 2006): 342–346.

Lesson 15. Data Analysis: Quality of Life

Practice Worksheet: *Practice with Data Analysis*

1 Bureau of Labor Statistics, "American Time Use Survey," www.bls.gov/news.release/atus.toc.htm (accessed February 1, 2009).

Background Reading: *What Do You Really Need?*

1 David G. Myers, "Happiness," in *Psychology*, Seventh Edition (New York: Worth Publishers, 2004).

Photo Credits

Thank you to the generous and talented photographers who contributed photos.

Front Cover

Girls with fruit on head by **Elizabeth Benedict Huttman**
Coins by **PhotoDisc, Inc.**
Seattle Center Fountain by **Jessica C Levine**
Zebras by **Kim Rakow Bernier**
Students working together by **Craig Snell**

Introduction

p. 7- Students collaborating by **Facing the Future**
p. 10- On the Double by **Jessica C Levine**

Lesson 1. Number Patterns: Waste & Recycling

p. 12- Boy recycling by **Gilda Wheeler**
p. 13- Recycling bin with crushed cans by **Desmond Talkington**
p. 14- Garbage can and recycling bins by **Nicole Conway**

Lesson 2. Introduction to Algebra: Poverty & Microcredit

p. 16- Bicycles in Asia by **PhotoDisc, Inc.**
p. 17- Man in shop by **Eddie Martinez**
p. 18- Child carrying basin on head **©iStockphoto/Sean_Warren**

Lesson 3. Modeling Integers: Population Growth

p. 21- Sunny island by **PhotoDisc, Inc.**
p. 22- Crowd in Hong Kong by **DECODE, Inc.**

Lesson 4. Solving Algebraic Equations: Food Choices

p. 23- Girl with basketball by **Michael Fletcher**
p. 24- School lunch by **Jay Morthland**
p. 25- People running race by **R. Ryan**
p. 26- Girls with fruit on head by **Elizabeth Benedict Huttman**

Lesson 5. Data & Graphs: Youth Conflict

p. 27- World Peace van by **Mike Rotenberg**
p. 28- Stop the Violence mural by **Tori Piccola**
p. 29- Students working together by **Craig Snell**
p. 30- Riot police **©iStockphoto/DeshaCAM**

Lesson 6. Number Theory: Consumption Choices

p. 31- Coffee mug and Styrofoam cup **©iStockphoto/terex and Chrystostom**
p. 32- Paper cup and stainless steel mug **©iStockphoto/davidp and bbehunin**
p. 33- Crushed cans by **PhotoDisc, Inc.**
p. 34- Sale window by **Laura Skelton**

Photo Credits, *continued*

Lesson 7. Rational Numbers: Financial Decisions

p. 36- National Debt Clock by **Chris Beckett**

p. 37- Coins by **PhotoDisc, Inc.**

p. 38- Dollar bills by **Tracy R. Olson**

Lesson 8. Proportion, Percent, & Probability: Global Health

p. 40- Multigenerational family ©iStockphoto/monkeybusinessimages

p. 41- Baby with mother by **PhotoDisc, Inc.**

p. 42- Health Center at Gunhill by **Mario Burger**

Lesson 9. Solving Inequalities: Carbon Emissions

p. 43- Cheeseburger ©iStockphoto/kcline

p. 44- Carbon footprints by **Christian Guthier/thisbluedot.net**

p. 46- Factory with smokestacks by **PhotoDisc, Inc.**

Lesson 10. Spatial Thinking: Solar Power

p. 48- Volunteers installing solar panels on roof by **Kate Davison, Greenpeace Southeast Asia**

p. 49- Houses with solar panel illustrations by **DECODE, Inc.**

p. 50- Wind turbine by **PhotoDisc,Inc.**

Lesson 11. Area & Transformations: Wildlife Habitats

p. 51- Snow leopard in zoo by **Heidi Connal**

p. 51- Mountains in Pakistan photo by **Bill Hogue, Courtesy of Snow Leopard Trust**

p. 51- Ajar Canyon in Afghanistan by **Abraham J Sheppard**

p. 52- Wild goat ©iStockphoto/sirius_r

p. 52- Snow leopard by **PhotoDisc, Inc.**

p. 54- Tumac Mountain South Cascades by **Jessica C Levine**

Lesson 12. Surface Area & Volume: Sustainable Design

p. 55- Milk container illustrations by **DECODE, Inc.**

p. 56- Juice carton illustrations by **DECODE, Inc.**

p. 56- Notebook ©iStockphoto/JLGutierrez

p. 57- Wall of windows at Seattle Public Library by **DECODE, Inc.**

Lesson 13. Linear Functions: Systems & Global Education

p. 58- Teddy bear ©iStockphoto/michael1959

p. 60- Students collaborating by **Facing the Future**

p. 61- Young children in Uganda by **Kim Rakow Bernier**

Lesson 14. Midpoint & Distance Formulas: Resource Distribution

p. 63- Model neighborhood by **Casey Broadwater**
p. 64- Seattle Center Fountain by **Jessica C Levine**

Lesson 15. Data Analysis: Quality of Life

p. 65- Woman scuba diving by **PhotoDisc, Inc.**
p. 67- Man and child at rally in Washington, D.C. by **Brian Greer**